MAD LIBS®

GOING MAD FOR
MAD LIBS

PSS!
PRICE STERN SLOAN
An Imprint of Penguin Random House

PRICE STERN SLOAN
Penguin Young Readers Group
An Imprint of Penguin Random House LLC

Mad Libs format and text copyright © 1998, 2009, 2011, 2016 by Price Stern Sloan,
an imprint of Penguin Random House LLC. All rights reserved.

Concept created by Roger Price & Leonard Stern

Going Mad for Mad Libs published in 2016
by Price Stern Sloan, an imprint of Penguin Random House LLC,
345 Hudson Street, New York, New York 10014. Printed in the USA.

ISBN 9781101950258

3 5 7 9 10 8 6 4

MAD LIBS®

MAD MAD MAD MAD MAD LIBS

By Roger Price and Leonard Stern

PRICE STERN SLOAN

An Imprint of Penguin Random House

MAD LIBS
INSTRUCTIONS

MAD LIBS® is a game for people who don't like games!
It can be played by one, two, three, four, or forty.

• RIDICULOUSLY SIMPLE DIRECTIONS

In this tablet you will find stories containing blank spaces where words are left out. One player, the **READER**, selects one of these stories. The **READER** does not tell anyone what the story is about. Instead, he/she asks the other players, the **WRITERS**, to give him/her words. These words are used to fill in the blank spaces in the story.

• TO PLAY

The **READER** asks each **WRITER** in turn to call out a word—an adjective or a noun or whatever the space calls for—and uses them to fill in the blank spaces in the story. The result is a **MAD LIBS®** game.

When the **READER** then reads the completed **MAD LIBS®** game to the other players, they will discover that they have written a story that is fantastic, screamingly funny, shocking, silly, crazy, or just plain dumb—depending upon which words each **WRITER** called out.

• EXAMPLE (*Before* and *After*)

" _____ !" he said _____
    EXCLAMATION   ADVERB

as he jumped into his convertible _____ and
                                          NOUN

drove off with his _____ wife.
                        ADJECTIVE

" *Ouch!* !" he said *Stupidly*
    EXCLAMATION   ADVERB

as he jumped into his convertible *cat* and
                                          NOUN

drove off with his *brave* wife.
                        ADJECTIVE

In case you have forgotten what adjectives, adverbs, nouns, and verbs are, here is a quick review:

An **ADJECTIVE** describes something or somebody. *Lumpy, soft, ugly, messy,* and *short* are adjectives.

An **ADVERB** tells how something is done. It modifies a verb and usually ends in "ly." *Modestly, stupidly, greedily,* and *carefully* are adverbs.

A **NOUN** is the name of a person, place, or thing. *Sidewalk, umbrella, bridle, bathtub,* and *nose* are nouns.

A **VERB** is an action word. *Run, pitch, jump,* and *swim* are verbs. Put the verbs in past tense if the directions say PAST TENSE. *Ran, pitched, jumped,* and *swam* are verbs in the past tense.

When we ask for a **PLACE**, we mean any sort of place: a country or city *(Spain, Cleveland)* or a room *(bathroom, kitchen)*.

An **EXCLAMATION** or **SILLY WORD** is any sort of funny sound, gasp, grunt, or outcry, like *Wow!, Ouch!, Whomp!, Ick!,* and *Gadzooks!*

When we ask for specific words, like a **NUMBER**, a **COLOR**, an **ANIMAL**, or a **PART OF THE BODY**, we mean a word that is one of those things, like *seven, blue, horse,* or *head*.

When we ask for a **PLURAL**, it means more than one. For example, *cat* pluralized is *cats*.

MAD LIBS® is fun to play with friends, but you can also play it by yourself! To begin with, DO NOT look at the story on the page below. Fill in the blanks on this page with the words called for. Then, using the words you have selected, fill in the blank spaces in the story.

Now you've created your own hilarious MAD LIBS® game!

NURSERY RHYMES

ADJECTIVE _____

ADVERB _____

PART OF THE BODY (PLURAL) _____

PART OF THE BODY (PLURAL) _____

ADJECTIVE _____

NOUN _____

VERB _____

TYPE OF LIQUID _____

NOUN _____

VERB ENDING IN "ING" _____

NOUN _____

ADJECTIVE _____

ADJECTIVE _____

PLURAL NOUN _____

PLURAL NOUN _____

NOUN _____

VERB (PAST TENSE) _____

PART OF THE BODY (PLURAL) _____

ADJECTIVE _____

VERB _____

NOUN _____

ADJECTIVE _____

MAD LIBS
NURSERY RHYMES

When some _____ school students were asked what
                    ADJECTIVE

nursery rhymes popped _____ into their _____
                            ADVERB   PART OF BODY (PLURAL)

or were on the tip of their _____, these were
                                    PART OF BODY (PLURAL)

their _____ answers:
        ADJECTIVE

1. Jack and Jill went up the _____ to _____ a pail
                                    NOUN   VERB

   of _____. Jack fell down and broke his _____
        TYPE OF LIQUID   NOUN

   and Jill came _____ after.
                    VERB ENDING IN "ING"

2. Mary, Mary, quite contrary, how does your _____
                                                        NOUN

   grow? With _____ bells and _____ shells and
                ADJECTIVE   ADJECTIVE

   _____ all in a row.
        PLURAL NOUN

3. Three blind _____, see how they run. They all went
                    PLURAL NOUN

   after the _____'s wife, who _____ off their
                NOUN   VERB (PAST TENSE)

   _____ with a/an _____ knife. Did you
        PART OF BODY (PLURAL)   ADJECTIVE

   ever _____ such a/an _____ in your life as
            VERB   NOUN

   three _____ mice?
            ADJECTIVE

MAD LIBS® is fun to play with friends, but you can also play it by yourself! To begin with, DO NOT look at the story on the page below. Fill in the blanks on this page with the words called for. Then, using the words you have selected, fill in the blank spaces in the story.

Now you've created your own hilarious MAD LIBS® game!

A VISIT TO THE DENTIST

PLURAL NOUN _____

PERSON IN ROOM (LAST NAME)_____

ADJECTIVE _____

NOUN _____

NOUN _____

PART OF THE BODY _____

PART OF THE BODY _____

PLURAL NOUN_____

NOUN _____

NOUN _____

EXCLAMATION _____

NOUN _____

NOUN _____

NOUN _____

VERB _____

NOUN _____

ADJECTIVE _____

NOUN _____

MAD LIBS®

A VISIT TO THE DENTIST

A one-act play to be performed by two _____ *in this room.*
PLURAL NOUN

PATIENT: Thank you so very much for seeing me, Doctor

_____ , on such _____ notice.
PERSON IN ROOM (LAST NAME)   ADJECTIVE

DENTIST: What is your problem, young _____ ?
NOUN

PATIENT: I have a pain in my upper _____ , which
NOUN

is giving me a severe _____ ache.
PART OF THE BODY

DENTIST: Let me take a look. Open your _____ wide.
PART OF THE BODY

Good. Now I'm going to tap your _____ with my _____ .
PLURAL NOUN   NOUN

PATIENT: Shouldn't you give me a/an _____ killer?
NOUN

DENTIST: It's not necessary yet. _____ ! I think I see
EXCLAMATION

a/an _____ in your upper _____ .
NOUN   NOUN

PATIENT: Are you going to pull my _____ out?
NOUN

DENTIST: No. I'm going to _____ your tooth and put in
VERB

a temporary _____ .
NOUN

PATIENT: When do I come back for the _____ filling?
ADJECTIVE

DENTIST: A day after I cash your _____ .
NOUN

MAD LIBS® is fun to play with friends, but you can also play it by yourself! To begin with, DO NOT look at the story on the page below. Fill in the blanks on this page with the words called for. Then, using the words you have selected, fill in the blank spaces in the story.

Now you've created your own hilarious MAD LIBS® game!

THE OSCARS

PLURAL NOUN _____

NOUN _____

NOUN _____

NOUN _____

ADJECTIVE _____

VERB _____

ADJECTIVE _____

PERSON IN ROOM _____

NOUN _____

PART OF BODY _____

ADJECTIVE _____

NOUN _____

ADJECTIVE _____

ADJECTIVE _____

ADJECTIVE _____

ADJECTIVE _____

NOUN _____

VERB ENDING IN "ING" _____

ADJECTIVE _____

PLURAL NOUN _____

MAD LIBS
THE OSCARS

Thank you, ladies and _____. I'm so nervous.
PLURAL NOUN

My _____ is beating a/an _____ a minute.
NOUN   NOUN

I didn't prepare a/an _____. I never expected to win
NOUN

this _____ Oscar. I have so many people to
ADJECTIVE

_____. First and foremost, my _____
VERB   ADJECTIVE

co-star — _____ — who was always in my dressing
PERSON IN ROOM

_____, held my _____ when
NOUN   PART OF BODY

I was in trouble, and never failed to compliment me or give me a/an

_____ pat on my _____ when I did well.
ADJECTIVE   NOUN

I also want to thank my _____ director, my_____
ADJECTIVE   ADJECTIVE

producer, and of course, the _____ writer of the
ADJECTIVE

screenplay. Most of all, I want to thank you, my _____
ADJECTIVE

fans, and all the members of the Motion Picture _____
NOUN

who were responsible for my _____ this
VERB ENDING IN "ING"

_____ award. Bless your _____.
ADJECTIVE   PLURAL NOUN

From MAD MAD MAD MAD MAD LIBS® • Copyright © 1998 by Price Stern Sloan,
an imprint of Penguin Random House LLC, 345 Hudson Street, New York, NY 10014.

MAD LIBS® is fun to play with friends, but you can also play it by yourself! To begin with, DO NOT look at the story on the page below. Fill in the blanks on this page with the words called for. Then, using the words you have selected, fill in the blank spaces in the story.

Now you've created your own hilarious MAD LIBS® game!

BRINGING HOME THE GOOD ... OR IS IT BAD? ... NEWS

PERSON IN ROOM _____

ADJECTIVE _____

LETTER OF THE ALPHABET _____

LETTER OF THE ALPHABET _____

PLURAL NOUN _____

NOUN _____

NOUN _____

PART OF THE BODY _____

NOUN _____

ADJECTIVE _____

NOUN _____

NOUN _____

SAME PERSON IN ROOM _____

ADJECTIVE _____

ADJECTIVE _____

NOUN _____

ADVERB _____

PART OF THE BODY _____

NOUN _____

ADJECTIVE _____

ANOTHER PERSON IN ROOM (LAST NAME)_____

OCCUPATION_____

MAD  LIBS

BRINGING HOME THE GOOD ...OR IS IT BAD?...NEWS

Dear Parent,

Here is _____'s report card for the _____
                    PERSON IN ROOM   ADJECTIVE

eighth grade. He/she has received a/an _____
                                          LETTER OF THE ALPHABET

in English, a/an _____ in Mathematics, and an
                  LETTER OF THE ALPHABET

"A" in Social _____. Unfortunately, we could not
                 PLURAL NOUN

give a passing _____ in _____ Education
                    NOUN   NOUN

because his/her broken _____ prevented the taking of
                          PART OF THE BODY

the final _____. This _____ class can
              NOUN   ADJECTIVE

be made up in our summer _____. The school
                              NOUN

believes a "parent-_____ conference" is necessary to
                        NOUN

discuss _____'s _____ behavior.
          SAME PERSON IN ROOM   ADJECTIVE

He/She continues to draw_____ pictures on the bathroom
                            ADJECTIVE

_____ and talks _____ behind the teacher's
        NOUN   ADVERB

_____. Please call the principal's _____
   PART OF THE BODY   NOUN

for a/an _____ appointment immediately.
             ADJECTIVE

                    Sincerely,

                    Ms. _____
                          ANOTHER PERSON IN ROOM (LAST NAME)

                    Head _____
                              OCCUPATION

From MAD MAD MAD MAD MAD LIBS® • Copyright © 1998 by Price Stern Sloan,
an imprint of Penguin Random House LLC, 345 Hudson Street, New York, NY 10014.

MAD LIBS® is fun to play with friends, but you can also play it by yourself! To begin with, DO NOT look at the story on the page below. Fill in the blanks on this page with the words called for. Then, using the words you have selected, fill in the blank spaces in the story.

Now you've created your own hilarious MAD LIBS® game!

CULTURAL STUFF

PLURAL NOUN _____

PLURAL NOUN _____

PART OF THE BODY (PLURAL) _____

ADJECTIVE _____

NOUN _____

VERB ENDING IN "ING" _____

ADJECTIVE _____

PERSON IN ROOM _____

PLURAL NOUN _____

NOUN _____

PLURAL NOUN _____

PLURAL NOUN _____

ADJECTIVE _____

ADJECTIVE _____

ADJECTIVE _____

PLURAL NOUN _____

ANOTHER PERSON IN ROOM_____

PLURAL NOUN _____

NOUN _____

MAD LIBS®
CULTURAL STUFF

I. BALLET

Ballet companies are springing up like _____ all
_{PLURAL NOUN}

over the country. Ballet is a form of dance in which male and female

_____ tell a story through movement of their arms
_{PLURAL NOUN}

and _____ to _____. music. Two of the best-
_{PART OF THE BODY (PLURAL)} _{ADJECTIVE}

known ballets are _____ *Lake* and _____ *Beauty*.
_{NOUN} _{VERB ENDING IN "ING"}

II. OPERA

Thanks to the three _____ tenors, Pavarotti, Domingo,
_{ADJECTIVE}

and _____ , opera is once again playing to packed
_{PERSON IN ROOM}

_____ in every major _____ in the country.
_{PLURAL NOUN} _{NOUN}

The sales of their tapes and compact _____ have established
_{PLURAL NOUN}

this trio of tenors as America's favorite _____ .
_{PLURAL NOUN}

III. SYMPHONY

Classical music is making a/an _____ comeback these
_{ADJECTIVE}

days. Symphony orchestras led by _____ conductors
_{ADJECTIVE}

are once again playing the _____ melodies of such musical
_{ADJECTIVE}

_____ as Bach, Beethoven and _____ .
_{PLURAL NOUN} _{ANOTHER PERSON IN ROOM}

Once again, auditoriums are filled with _____ of all ages,
_{PLURAL NOUN}

who rejoice in listening to a violin solo or a _____ concerto.
_{NOUN}

MAD LIBS® is fun to play with friends, but you can also play it by yourself! To begin with, DO NOT look at the story on the page below. Fill in the blanks on this page with the words called for. Then, using the words you have selected, fill in the blank spaces in the story.

Now you've created your own hilarious MAD LIBS® game!

INSTRUCTIONS FOR THE BABYSITTER

ADJECTIVE _____

PLURAL NOUN _____

PLURAL NOUN _____

PLURAL NOUN _____

PLURAL NOUN _____

NOUN _____

ADVERB _____

NOUN _____

TYPE OF LIQUID _____

VERB _____

NOUN _____

NOUN _____

ADJECTIVE _____

ADJECTIVE _____

NOUN _____

MAD☺LIBS®
INSTRUCTIONS FOR THE BABYSITTER

The boys can watch an hour of _____ television
                                    ADJECTIVE

before turning off the _____ in their room. Make sure
                        PLURAL NOUN

they do not watch any violent _____ or adult _____.
                                PLURAL NOUN   PLURAL NOUN

If there are any phone _____, do not identify yourself as
                        PLURAL NOUN

the _____-sitter. Take a message. Write it _____
      NOUN   ADVERB

on the _____ provided.
        NOUN

Remember, the baby gets his warm _____ around six o'clock.
                                  TYPE OF LIQUID

If the baby starts to _____ in his _____, be sure
                        VERB   NOUN

to change his diaper before you put him back in his _____.
                                                      NOUN

If you have any _____ questions or _____
                  ADJECTIVE   ADJECTIVE

problems, please page us on our _____.
                                  NOUN

Good luck!

MAD LIBS® is fun to play with friends, but you can also play it by yourself! To begin with, DO NOT look at the story on the page below. Fill in the blanks on this page with the words called for. Then, using the words you have selected, fill in the blank spaces in the story.

Now you've created your own hilarious MAD LIBS® game!

ADVICE COLUMN

PERSON IN ROOM (FIRST NAME) _____

ADJECTIVE _____

NUMBER _____

NOUN _____

NOUN _____

PLURAL NOUN _____

VERB ENDING IN "ING" _____

NOUN _____

NUMBER _____

SAME PERSON IN ROOM (FIRST NAME) _____

NOUN _____

ADJECTIVE _____

NOUN _____

PLURAL NOUN _____

NOUN _____

ADVERB _____

NOUN _____

NOUN _____

NOUN _____

VERB _____

ADJECTIVE _____

NOUN _____

NOUN _____

MAD LIBS®
ADVICE COLUMN

Dear _____ ,
PERSON IN ROOM (FIRST NAME)

My _____ daughter, who is only _____ years old,
ADJECTIVE   NUMBER

wants to wear a mini _____ with a bare _____ .
NOUN   NOUN

She claims all the other _____ her age are _____
PLURAL NOUN   VERB ENDING IN "ING"

them. What to do?

Signed,
An anxious _____
NOUN

Dear "Anxious,"

Take my advice and ground your daughter for _____ days.
NUMBER

Dear _____ ,
SAME PERSON IN ROOM (FIRST NAME)

My oldest _____ is a/an _____ slob. As
NOUN   ADJECTIVE

often as I try, I can never get him to wash his _____ , brush
NOUN

his _____ , or comb his _____ before going to
PLURAL NOUN   NOUN

school. He also _____ refuses to take a bath or a/an
ADVERB

_____ , clean up his _____ , or make up
NOUN   NOUN

the very _____ he sleeps in. How can I _____ ?
NOUN   VERB

Signed,
A/an _____ Mother
ADJECTIVE

Dear "Mother,"

You better clean that _____ up before he turns into a
NOUN

filthy ball of _____ .
NOUN

From MAD MAD MAD MAD MAD LIBS® • Copyright © 1998 by Price Stern Sloan,
an imprint of Penguin Random House LLC, 345 Hudson Street, New York, NY 10014.

MAD LIBS® is fun to play with friends, but you can also play it by yourself! To begin with, DO NOT look at the story on the page below. Fill in the blanks on this page with the words called for. Then, using the words you have selected, fill in the blank spaces in the story.

Now you've created your own hilarious MAD LIBS® game!

LOST AND FOUND

ADJECTIVE _____

NOUN _____

PART OF THE BODY (PLURAL) _____

ADJECTIVE _____

PERSON IN ROOM (FIRST NAME) _____

NOUN _____

ADVERB _____

NOUN _____

PLURAL NOUN _____

ADJECTIVE _____

TYPE OF VEGETABLE _____

NOUN _____

NOUN _____

ADJECTIVE _____

PART OF THE BODY _____

NOUN _____

ADJECTIVE _____

VERB ENDING IN "ING" _____

ADJECTIVE _____

NOUN _____

ADJECTIVE _____

NOUN _____

MAD LIBS
LOST AND FOUND

LOST

Dog. A black and _____ Cocker _____ with
         ADJECTIVE   NOUN

deep brown _____ and a very _____
              PART OF THE BODY (PLURAL)   ADJECTIVE

tail. Answers to the name of _____.
                              PERSON IN ROOM (FIRST NAME)

LOST

A solid gold _____ with a/an _____
                NOUN   ADVERB

carved wooden _____ hanging from it. Reward of
                   NOUN

50 _____ for the return of this _____ heirloom.
      PLURAL NOUN   ADJECTIVE

LOST

Seven _____ diamond _____ with a sterling
        TYPE OF VEGETABLE   NOUN

_____ clasp. Gift from _____ grandmother
      NOUN   ADJECTIVE

Owner is _____ broken. Generous _____
            PART OF THE BODY   NOUN

offered upon return.

FOUND

A/an _____ elephant in my _____ pool.
        ADJECTIVE   VERB ENDING IN "ING"

He has _____ marks on his hide, a short _____,
          ADJECTIVE   NOUN

and a very _____ trunk. Please come and get him.
                ADJECTIVE

He's eating me out of house and _____!
                                      NOUN

From MAD MAD MAD MAD MAD LIBS® • Copyright © 1998 by Price Stern Sloan,
an imprint of Penguin Random House LLC, 345 Hudson Street, New York, NY 10014.

MAD LIBS® is fun to play with friends, but you can also play it by yourself! To begin with, DO NOT look at the story on the page below. Fill in the blanks on this page with the words called for. Then, using the words you have selected, fill in the blank spaces in the story.

Now you've created your own hilarious MAD LIBS® game!

POOL ROOLS

NOUN _____

ADJECTIVE _____

ADJECTIVE _____

VERB ENDING IN "ING" _____

ADJECTIVE _____

PLURAL NOUN _____

ADJECTIVE _____

PLURAL NOUN _____

NUMBER _____

NOUN _____

NOUN _____

VERB ENDING IN "ING" _____

ADJECTIVE _____

NOUN _____

ADJECTIVE _____

PLURAL NOUN _____

ADVERB _____

PART OF THE BODY _____

ADJECTIVE _____

NOUN _____

ADJECTIVE _____

MAD LIBS®
POOL ROOLS

ATTENTION ALL SWIMMERS!

If you want to swim in this _____ or soak in our
                                   NOUN

_____ spa, you must follow these _____ rules.
   ADJECTIVE   ADJECTIVE

1. No nude _____ allowed. Men must wear
              VERB ENDING IN "ING"

   _____ shorts, and women must wear one-piece
            ADJECTIVE

   bathing _____ or _____ bikinis.
              PLURAL NOUN   ADJECTIVE

2. No _____ under the age of _____ are allowed in
          PLURAL NOUN   NUMBER

   the _____ unless accompanied by a/an _____ .
          NOUN   NOUN

3. _____ in the pool is only permitted in the
      VERB ENDING IN "ING"

   _____ end and only when a life-_____
            ADJECTIVE   NOUN

   is on duty.

4. People with _____ hair must wear bathing _____ .
                   ADJECTIVE   PLURAL NOUN

WARNING! If you plan to sunbathe, _____ cover your
                                            ADVERB

arms, legs, and _____ with a/an _____
                   PART OF THE BODY   ADJECTIVE

lotion. You don't want to get a/an _____ burn!
                                        NOUN

Have a/an _____ day!
                   ADJECTIVE

MAD LIBS® is fun to play with friends, but you can also play it by yourself! To begin with, DO NOT look at the story on the page below. Fill in the blanks on this page with the words called for. Then, using the words you have selected, fill in the blank spaces in the story.

Now you've created your own hilarious MAD LIBS® game!

WHAT'S IN A NAME?

PLURAL NOUN _____

NOUN _____

NOUN _____

PART OF THE BODY _____

PLURAL NOUN _____

ADVERB _____

NOUN _____

ADJECTIVE _____

ADJECTIVE _____

NOUN _____

NOUN _____

PERSON IN ROOM (LAST NAME) _____

NOUN _____

NOUN _____

ADJECTIVE _____

MAD LIBS
WHAT'S IN A NAME?

William Shakespeare is regarded by scholars and _____
                                                    PLURAL NOUN

alike as the greatest playwright and _____ ever to put
                                           NOUN

pen to _____. Although he wrote in his native
            NOUN

_____, Shakespeare has been translated into twelve
PART OF THE BODY

different _____ and his plays and poems are _____
           PLURAL NOUN   ADVERB

read and performed everywhere in the world. Hamlet's soliloquy —

which begins "To be or not to be, that is the _____," —
                                                    NOUN

has been delivered on stage by more _____ actors
                                          ADJECTIVE

than any other _____ _____ ever written.
                  ADJECTIVE   NOUN

Among Shakespeare's greatest plays are *Hamlet*, *Romeo and Juliet*,

The _____ *of Venice*, *King* _____,
         NOUN   PERSON IN ROOM (LAST NAME)

A Midsummer Night's _____, and *The Taming of*
                          NOUN

the _____. We could go on, but we must leave. As Romeo
         NOUN

said to Juliet, "Parting is such _____ sorrow."
                                    ADJECTIVE

MAD LIBS® is fun to play with friends, but you can also play it by yourself! To begin with, DO NOT look at the story on the page below. Fill in the blanks on this page with the words called for. Then, using the words you have selected, fill in the blank spaces in the story.

Now you've created your own hilarious MAD LIBS® game!

A GOOD NIGHT'S SLEEP

ADJECTIVE _____

ADJECTIVE _____

PART OF THE BODY (PLURAL) _____

NOUN _____

ADVERB _____

ADVERB _____

PLURAL NOUN _____

ADJECTIVE _____

VERB _____

PLURAL NOUN _____

PART OF THE BODY _____

ADJECTIVE _____

TYPE OF LIQUID _____

NOUN _____

NOUN _____

ANIMAL (PLURAL) _____

NOUN _____

PART OF THE BODY _____

MAD LIBS

A GOOD NIGHT'S SLEEP

Here are five _____ suggestions to follow if you want
                    ADJECTIVE

a/an _____ night's sleep:
     ADJECTIVE

1. Open a window and fill your _____ with fresh
                                PART OF THE BODY (PLURAL)

   _____ and then, exhale _____ .
         NOUN   ADVERB

2. Exercise _____ at least 15 _____ a day.
              ADVERB   PLURAL NOUN

   Doctors and _____ therapists suggest a combination
                   ADJECTIVE

   of push-ups and _____-ups, jumping _____ ,
                         VERB   PLURAL NOUN

   and, of course, deep _____ bends.
                          PART OF THE BODY

3. Drink a/an _____ glass of warm _____
                 ADJECTIVE   TYPE OF LIQUID

   a half hour before turning off your _____ and going to
                                            NOUN

   _____ .
          NOUN

4. If all else fails, count _____ jumping over a/an
                             ANIMAL (PLURAL)

   _____ .
          NOUN

5. WARNING: Never go to bed on a full _____ .
                                         PART OF THE BODY

From MAD MAD MAD MAD MAD LIBS® • Copyright © 1998 by Price Stern Sloan,
an imprint of Penguin Random House LLC, 345 Hudson Street, New York, NY 10014.

MAD LIBS® is fun to play with friends, but you can also play it by yourself! To begin with, DO NOT look at the story on the page below. Fill in the blanks on this page with the words called for. Then, using the words you have selected, fill in the blank spaces in the story.

Now you've created your own hilarious MAD LIBS® game!

LOOK IT UP

ADJECTIVE _____

NOUN _____

NOUN _____

PLURAL NOUN _____

ADVERB _____

ADVERB _____

NOUN _____

NOUN _____

NOUN _____

NOUN _____

PLURAL NOUN _____

PLURAL NOUN _____

ADVERB _____

NOUN _____

NOUN _____

NOUN _____

NOUN _____

NOUN _____

NOUN _____

MAD LIBS®
LOOK IT UP

A/An _____ dictionary is the essential reference
ADJECTIVE

_____ for home, school, or _____ .
NOUN   NOUN

A dictionary not only defines _____ , but tells you how
PLURAL NOUN

to spell words _____ and how to pronounce them
ADVERB

_____ . Dictionaries are available in local _____
ADVERB   NOUN

stores or, if necessary, you can order one with a/an _____ card
NOUN

over the Internet. For the average _____ , a medium-sized
NOUN

dictionary is best. For researchers, an unabridged _____ ,
NOUN

which has more than 200,000 _____ will be needed.
PLURAL NOUN

For those who can't remember the meaning of any _____ ,
PLURAL NOUN

a pocket-sized dictionary works _____ . These dictionaries
ADVERB

are small enough to fit in a woman's _____ , the pocket of a
NOUN

man's _____ , or a kid's back _____ . As
NOUN   NOUN

Henry Wadsworth Longefellow, the famous _____ wrote,
NOUN

"I'd rather go without food in my _____ than go
NOUN

without a dictionary on my _____ shelf."
NOUN

MAD LIBS® is fun to play with friends, but you can also play it by yourself! To begin with, DO NOT look at the story on the page below. Fill in the blanks on this page with the words called for. Then, using the words you have selected, fill in the blank spaces in the story.

Now you've created your own hilarious MAD LIBS® game!

COFFEEHOUSES

NOUN _____

NOUN _____

ADJECTIVE _____

ADJECTIVE _____

NOUN _____

ADJECTIVE _____

ADJECTIVE _____

NOUN _____

PLURAL NOUN _____

TYPE OF LIQUID _____

PLURAL NOUN _____

VERB _____

NOUN _____

PLURAL NOUN _____

ADJECTIVE _____

ANOTHER TYPE OF LIQUID _____

PLURAL NOUN _____

PART OF THE BODY _____

VERB _____

PLURAL NOUN _____

PLURAL NOUN _____

PART OF THE BODY _____

MAD LIBS
COFFEEHOUSES

Coffeehouses are in! Gone are the local corner _____
NOUN

and the neighborhood ice-cream _____. It doesn't matter
NOUN

if you live in a/an _____ city or a/an _____
ADJECTIVE   ADJECTIVE

town, there is bound to be a coffee _____ in your
NOUN

_____ neighborhood. Coffeehouses have become the place
ADJECTIVE

where _____ friends gather, sit, and chew the _____,
ADJECTIVE   NOUN

remembering the good old _____ as they sip their steaming
PLURAL NOUN

cups of _____. Coffeehouses cater to busy business
TYPE OF LIQUID

_____, who use them to _____ million
PLURAL NOUN   VERB

_____ deals. Coffeehouses are also favorite spots for single
NOUN

men and _____, who love to linger over their mugs of
PLURAL NOUN

_____ _____ as they watch the attractive
ADJECTIVE   ANOTHER TYPE OF LIQUID

_____ go by, hoping to catch his or her _____,
PLURAL NOUN   PART OF THE BODY

and maybe even _____ a date. Most evenings, coffeehouses
VERB

are filled by young lovers drinking out of each others' _____
PLURAL NOUN

as they whisper sweet _____ in each other's _____.
PLURAL NOUN   PART OF THE BODY

MAD LIBS® is fun to play with friends, but you can also play it by yourself! To begin with, DO NOT look at the story on the page below. Fill in the blanks on this page with the words called for. Then, using the words you have selected, fill in the blank spaces in the story.

Now you've created your own hilarious MAD LIBS® game!

IT'S ABOUT TIME

PLURAL NOUN_____

PLURAL NOUN_____

PLURAL NOUN_____

NUMBER_____

PLURAL NOUN_____

NOUN _____

NOUN _____

NOUN _____

NOUN _____

PART OF THE BODY _____

LETTER OF THE ALPHABET _____

PLURAL NOUN_____

PLURAL NOUN_____

PLURAL NOUN_____

PART OF THE BODY _____

PART OF THE BODY _____

NUMBER_____

ADJECTIVE _____

NOUN _____

MAD LIBS
IT'S ABOUT TIME

Thousands of _____ ago, there were calendars that
              PLURAL NOUN

enabled the ancient _____ to divide a year into twelve
                    PLURAL NOUN

_____ , each month into _____ weeks, and each
      PLURAL NOUN   NUMBER

week into seven _____ . At first, people told time by a
                PLURAL NOUN

sun clock, sometimes known as the _____ dial. Ultimately,
                                     NOUN

they invented the great timekeeping devices of today, such as the

grandfather _____ , the pocket _____ , the alarm
              NOUN   NOUN

_____ , and, of course, the _____ watch.
    NOUN   PART OF BODY

Children learn about clocks and time almost before they learn their

AB _____ 's. They are taught that a day consists of 24
   LETTER OF THE ALPHABET

_____ , an hour has 60 _____ , and a minute has 60
PLURAL NOUN   PLURAL NOUN

_____ . By the time they are in kindergarten, they know if
PLURAL NOUN

the big _____ is at twelve and the little _____
        PART OF THE BODY -   PART OF THE BODY

is at three, that it is _____ o'clock. I wish we could continue this
                       NUMBER

_____ lesson, but we've run out of _____ .
  ADJECTIVE   NOUN

From MAD MAD MAD MAD MAD LIBS® • Copyright © 1998 by Price Stern Sloan,
an imprint of Penguin Random House LLC, 345 Hudson Street, New York, NY 10014.

MAD LIBS® is fun to play with friends, but you can also play it by yourself! To begin with, DO NOT look at the story on the page below. Fill in the blanks on this page with the words called for. Then, using the words you have selected, fill in the blank spaces in the story.

Now you've created your own hilarious MAD LIBS® game!

LETTERS PARENTS HOPE GET LOST IN THE MAIL

ADVERB _____

NOUN _____

NOUN _____

ADJECTIVE _____

COLOR _____

NOUN _____

PART OF THE BODY _____

PERSON IN ROOM (MALE) _____

NOUN _____

ADJECTIVE _____

PERSON IN ROOM (FEMALE) _____

ADVERB _____

NOUN _____

PLURAL NOUN _____

ADJECTIVE _____

NOUN _____

PART OF THE BODY _____

NUMBER _____

NOUN _____

ADJECTIVE _____

ANOTHER PERSON IN ROOM (MALE) _____

ANIMAL _____

PART OF THE BODY _____

PART OF THE BODY _____

VERB _____

SAME ANIMAL _____

MAD LIBS

LETTERS PARENTS HOPE GET LOST IN THE MAIL

Dear Folks,

I'm in L.A. It is _____ awesome. Yesterday, I met the greatest
                        ADVERB

_____. He plays _____ with a/an _____
    NOUN   NOUN   ADJECTIVE

band. He has _____ hair and wears a/an _____
                    COLOR   NOUN

in his _____. I can't wait for you to meet
              PART OF BODY

_____, the _____ of my dreams.
    PERSON IN ROOM (MALE)   NOUN

                Your _____ daughter,
                          ADJECTIVE

              _____
                    PERSON IN ROOM (FEMALE)

Dear Folks,

Please send money as _____ as possible. I found a really great
                            ADVERB

surf _____ for only 150 _____. I borrowed the money from
      NOUN   PLURAL NOUN

my _____ girlfriend, who is a life _____ at the beach and is
      ADJECTIVE   NOUN

teaching me to surf nine-_____ waves. Although she is
                              PART OF THE BODY

_____ years older than I am, I know she's the right _____ for me.
NUMBER   NOUN

                Your _____ son,
                          ADJECTIVE

              _____
                    PERSON IN ROOM (MALE)

        (known to my beach friends as The _____)
                                                ANIMAL

Dear Folks,

For your information, I broke my _____ surfing, so I
                                      PART OF THE BODY

returned the surfboard. P.S. I used the money to get a tattoo on my

_____. You'll _____ it!
PART OF THE BODY   VERB

        Signed, The _____
                          SAME ANIMAL

MAD LIBS® is fun to play with friends, but you can also play it by yourself! To begin with, DO NOT look at the story on the page below. Fill in the blanks on this page with the words called for. Then, using the words you have selected, fill in the blank spaces in the story.

Now you've created your own hilarious MAD LIBS® game!

A CONCERT REVIEW

NOUN _____

FOOD _____

PLURAL NOUN _____

PLURAL NOUN _____

PLURAL NOUN _____

ADJECTIVE _____

NONSENSE WORD _____

ADJECTIVE _____

NOUN _____

PLURAL NOUN _____

PART OF THE BODY (PLURAL) _____

PERSON IN ROOM _____

ANIMAL _____

PLURAL NOUN _____

PART OF THE BODY _____

PLURAL NOUN _____

ADVERB _____

PLURAL NOUN _____

NOUN _____

MAD LIBS®

A CONCERT REVIEW

Throughout last night's _____, the cheering for the
<u>NOUN</u>

performance of Pearl _____ was so deafening, you had to
<u>FOOD</u>

hold your _____ over your _____ . Many well-
<u>PLURAL NOUN</u>   <u>PLURAL NOUN</u>

known _____ are calling it the _____ concert
<u>PLURAL NOUN</u>   <u>ADJECTIVE</u>

of the decade. For their opening number, the band played their hit

song, "_____," followed by their _____ rendition
<u>NONSENSE WORD</u>   <u>ADJECTIVE</u>

of "I Can't Get No _____." Then, as a tribute to the Beatles,
<u>NOUN</u>

they played several _____ from the hit album, *Sergeant*
<u>PLURAL NOUN</u>

Pepper's Lonely _____ *Club Band.* Unfortunately,
<u>PART OF THE BODY (PLURAL)</u>

throughout the performance, lead singer _____
<u>PERSON IN ROOM</u>

moved about the stage like a caged _____, singing at the top
<u>ANIMAL</u>

of his/her _____, giving this critic a terrible _____
<u>PLURAL NOUN</u>   <u>PART OF THE BODY</u>

ache. However, the concert ended with the audience standing on

their _____ and applauding _____, forcing
<u>PLURAL NOUN</u>   <u>ADVERB</u>

the group to come back for three _____ before the
<u>PLURAL NOUN</u>

_____ finally came down.
<u>NOUN</u>

From MAD MAD MAD MAD MAD LIBS® • Copyright © 1998 by Price Stern Sloan,
an imprint of Penguin Random House LLC, 345 Hudson Street, New York, NY 10014.

MAD LIBS® is fun to play with friends, but you can also play it by yourself! To begin with, DO NOT look at the story on the page below. Fill in the blanks on this page with the words called for. Then, using the words you have selected, fill in the blank spaces in the story.

Now you've created your own hilarious MAD LIBS® game!

NEXT-DOOR NEIGHBORS

PLURAL NOUN _____

NOUN _____

ADJECTIVE _____

NOUN _____

NOUN _____

NOUN _____

ADJECTIVE _____

NOUN _____

ADJECTIVE _____

TYPE OF FOOD _____

ADVERB _____

NOUN _____

NOUN _____

PLURAL NOUN _____

ADJECTIVE _____

NOUN _____

NOUN _____

PLURAL NOUN _____

ADJECTIVE _____

PLURAL NOUN _____

MAD LIBS
NEXT-DOOR NEIGHBORS

We have new _____ living in the _____ next
                    PLURAL NOUN   NOUN

door. He is a/an _____ salesman for a/an _____
                     ADJECTIVE   NOUN

company, and she teaches _____ in a private _____ .
                                   NOUN   NOUN

Last night, we were invited to their _____ home for a
                                            ADJECTIVE

potluck _____ . We brought a/an _____ _____
            NOUN   ADJECTIVE   TYPE OF FOOD

casserole. After dinner, we went into their _____ decorated
                                                    ADVERB

family _____ , sat in front of their roaring _____ , and
            NOUN   NOUN

toasted _____ . Before we left, our host insisted on taking
           PLURAL NOUN

out his _____ _____ — which we mistook for
           ADJECTIVE   NOUN

an ancient _____ — to play a few country _____
                 NOUN   PLURAL NOUN

on it. All in all, it was an _____ evening, and since then,
                                   ADJECTIVE

the four of us have become as thick as _____ .
                                              PLURAL NOUN

MAD LIBS® is fun to play with friends, but you can also play it by yourself! To begin with, DO NOT look at the story on the page below. Fill in the blanks on this page with the words called for. Then, using the words you have selected, fill in the blank spaces in the story.

Now you've created your own hilarious MAD LIBS® game!

CELLULAR PHONES

NUMBER_____

PLURAL NOUN_____

ADJECTIVE_____

VERB ENDING IN "ING"_____

NOUN_____

ADVERB_____

PART OF THE BODY_____

PLURAL NOUN_____

PLURAL NOUN_____

ADVERB_____

ADJECTIVE_____

NOUN_____

NUMBER_____

PLURAL NOUN_____

NOUN_____

VERB ENDING IN "ING"_____

NOUN_____

NOUN_____

NUMBER_____

ADJECTIVE_____

PLURAL NOUN_____

PART OF THE BODY_____

MAD LIBS
CELLULAR PHONES

A recent survey informs us that one out of every _____
NUMBER

_____ owns a/an _____ phone. Fortunately,
PLURAL NOUN   ADJECTIVE

_____ over a mobile _____ in recent years
VERB ENDING IN "ING"   NOUN

has improved _____ . Today, _____-held
ADVERB   PART OF THE BODY

_____ are all the rage. In restaurants, you find many
PLURAL NOUN

_____ talking _____ into their _____ phones
PLURAL NOUN   ADVERB   ADJECTIVE

as they eat their _____ . _____ percent of American
NOUN   NUMBER

_____ place their _____ calls from their
PLURAL NOUN   NOUN

cars as they are _____ to and from their home,
VERB ENDING IN "ING"

office, or _____ . Walking and talking are now the "in"
NOUN

_____ to do. Over _____ percent of Americans walk our
NOUN   NUMBER

_____ streets with a hand-held _____ pressed
ADJECTIVE   PLURAL NOUN

against their _____ .
PART OF THE BODY

From MAD MAD MAD MAD MAD LIBS® • Copyright © 1998 by Price Stern Sloan,
an imprint of Penguin Random House LLC, 345 Hudson Street, New York, NY 10014.

MAD LIBS® is fun to play with friends, but you can also play it by yourself! To begin with, DO NOT look at the story on the page below. Fill in the blanks on this page with the words called for. Then, using the words you have selected, fill in the blank spaces in the story.

Now you've created your own hilarious MAD LIBS® game!

LOVE LETTER

ADJECTIVE _____

NOUN _____

NOUN _____

ADJECTIVE _____

ADJECTIVE _____

NOUN _____

NOUN _____

NOUN _____

PART OF THE BODY _____

NOUN _____

NOUN _____

NOUN _____

ADJECTIVE _____

VERB _____

NOUN _____

PLURAL NOUN _____

PART OF THE BODY _____

PART OF THE BODY _____

NOUN _____

VERB _____

NOUN _____

NOUN _____

PART OF THE BODY _____

VERB _____

PERSON IN ROOM _____

MAD LIBS®
LOVE LETTER

My _____ darling,
        ADJECTIVE

I love you more than _____ itself. Each minute away from
                            NOUN

you is a/an _____, each hour a/an _____ eternity.
                  NOUN   ADJECTIVE

Without you, life is dull, boring, and _____. I feel like a
                                              ADJECTIVE

baby without my _____, a toddler without my teddy
                        NOUN

_____, a dog without its _____. I can't get you out
     NOUN   NOUN

of my _____. I can't stop thinking about the color of your
       PART OF THE BODY

_____, the way you wear your _____, the way you
     NOUN   NOUN

toss your _____, your _____ laugh, the way you
                NOUN   ADJECTIVE

_____ a joke. This morning, when the mail _____
     VERB   NOUN

brought your special delivery _____, my _____
                                    PLURAL NOUN   PART OF THE BODY

skipped a beat, my _____ was in my throat, and my
                        PART OF THE BODY

_____ trembled so much, I could hardly _____ your
     NOUN   VERB

_____. What you said set my _____ on fire. Do write
     NOUN   NOUN

again. Until then, I love you from the bottom of my _____.
                                                          PART OF THE BODY

I will _____ you always,
              VERB

_____
        PERSON IN ROOM

From MAD MAD MAD MAD MAD LIBS® • Copyright © 1998 by Price Stern Sloan,
an imprint of Penguin Random House LLC, 345 Hudson Street, New York, NY 10014.

Join the millions of Mad Libs fans creating wacky and wonderful stories on our apps!

Download Mad Libs today!

AD LIB
MAD LIBS

written by Leonard Stern

concept created by Roger Price & Leonard Stern

PSS!
PRICE STERN SLOAN
An Imprint of Penguin Random House

MAD LIBS

INSTRUCTIONS

MAD LIBS® is a game for people who don't like games!
It can be played by one, two, three, four, or forty.

• RIDICULOUSLY SIMPLE DIRECTIONS

In this tablet you will find stories containing blank spaces where words
are left out. One player, the READER, selects one of these stories. The
READER does not tell anyone what the story is about. Instead, he/she asks
the other players, the WRITERS, to give him/her words. These words are
used to fill in the blank spaces in the story.

• TO PLAY

The READER asks each WRITER in turn to call out a word—an adjective or
a noun or whatever the space calls for—and uses them to fill in the blank
spaces in the story. The result is a MAD LIBS® game.

When the READER then reads the completed MAD LIBS® game to the other
players, they will discover that they have written a story that is fantastic,
screamingly funny, shocking, silly, crazy, or just plain dumb—depending
upon which words each WRITER called out.

• EXAMPLE (*Before* and *After*)

" _____ !" he said _____
        EXCLAMATION   ADVERB

as he jumped into his convertible _____ and
                                                        NOUN

drove off with his _____ wife.
                              ADJECTIVE

" _____*Ouch*_____ !" he said _____*Stupidly*_____
        EXCLAMATION   ADVERB

as he jumped into his convertible _____*cat*_____ and
                                                NOUN

drove off with his _____*brave*_____ wife.
                              ADJECTIVE

MAD LIBS
QUICK REVIEW

In case you have forgotten what adjectives, adverbs, nouns, and verbs are, here is a quick review:

An ADJECTIVE describes something or somebody. *Lumpy*, *soft*, *ugly*, *messy*, and *short* are adjectives.

An ADVERB tells how something is done. It modifies a verb and usually ends in "ly." *Modestly*, *stupidly*, *greedily*, and *carefully* are adverbs.

A NOUN is the name of a person, place, or thing. *Sidewalk*, *umbrella*, *bridle*, *bathtub*, and *nose* are nouns.

A VERB is an action word. *Run*, *pitch*, *jump*, and *swim* are verbs. Put the verbs in past tense if the directions say PAST TENSE. *Ran*, *pitched*, *jumped*, and *swam* are verbs in the past tense.

When we ask for A PLACE, we mean any sort of place: a country or city (*Spain*, *Cleveland*) or a room (*bathroom*, *kitchen*).

An EXCLAMATION or SILLY WORD is any sort of funny sound, gasp, grunt, or outcry, like *Wow!*, *Ouch!*, *Whomp!*, *Ick!*, and *Gadzooks!*

When we ask for specific words, like a NUMBER, a COLOR, an ANIMAL, or a PART OF THE BODY, we mean a word that is one of those things, like *seven*, *blue*, *horse*, or *head*.

When we ask for a PLURAL, it means more than one. For example, *cat* pluralized is *cats*.

MAD LIBS® is fun to play with friends, but you can also play it by yourself! To begin with, DO NOT look at the story on the page below. Fill in the blanks on this page with the words called for. Then, using the words you have selected, fill in the blank spaces in the story.

Now you've created your own hilarious MAD LIBS® game!

LITTLE KNOWN FACTS ABOUT US PRESIDENTS, PART 1

PART OF THE BODY _____

NOUN _____

PART OF THE BODY (PLURAL) _____

NOUN _____

PLURAL NOUN _____

PART OF THE BODY (PLURAL) _____

ADJECTIVE _____

NOUN _____

ADJECTIVE _____

ADJECTIVE _____

PLURAL NOUN _____

PLURAL NOUN _____

PLURAL NOUN _____

• George Washington did not wear a wig on his _____,
                                                PART OF THE BODY

and he did not chop down a cherry _____; he did have
                                        NOUN

false _____, but they were not made of wood.
      PART OF THE BODY (PLURAL)

• Even when Abe Lincoln was not wearing his stovepipe

_____, he was the tallest of all the presidents, standing six
      NOUN

feet four _____ in his stocking _____.
          PLURAL NOUN   PART OF THE BODY (PLURAL)

• Thomas Jefferson composed the _____ epitaph for his
                                    ADJECTIVE

tombstone. He wanted to be remembered as the author of the

_____ of Independence and failed to mention that he had
    NOUN

been a/an _____ president of the United States.
            ADJECTIVE

• Thomas Jefferson and John Adams had a/an _____ history.
                                                ADJECTIVE

They were close friends, then enemies, and then _____
                                                    PLURAL NOUN

again until the ends of their _____.
                                PLURAL NOUN

• Grover Cleveland was the only president whose two _____
                                                        PLURAL NOUN

were not consecutive. He was our twenty-second *and* twenty-fourth

chief of state.

MAD LIBS® is fun to play with friends, but you can also play it by yourself! To begin with, DO NOT look at the story on the page below. Fill in the blanks on this page with the words called for. Then, using the words you have selected, fill in the blank spaces in the story.

Now you've created your own hilarious MAD LIBS® game!

LITTLE KNOWN FACTS ABOUT US PRESIDENTS, PART 2

ADJECTIVE _____

PLURAL NOUN _____

LAST NAME _____

LAST NAME _____

NOUN _____

ADJECTIVE _____

PLURAL NOUN _____

NOUN _____

NUMBER _____

PLURAL NOUN _____

NOUN _____

ADJECTIVE _____

NOUN _____

NOUN _____

ADJECTIVE _____

• Harvard is a/an _____ university that has graduated the
ADJECTIVE

most American _____. Graduates include John Adams,
PLURAL NOUN

Theodore Roosevelt, John F. _____, George W. Bush,
LAST NAME

and Barack _____.
LAST NAME

• In 1833, Andrew Jackson became the first _____ to ride
NOUN

on a/an _____ train.
ADJECTIVE

• William H. Taft was the largest president ever, weighing in at more

than three hundred _____.
PLURAL NOUN

• James Madison was the shortest _____, at five feet _____
NOUN   NUMBER

inches. He also weighed the least, at just one hundred _____.
PLURAL NOUN

• At sixty-nine, Ronald Reagan was the oldest _____. The
NOUN

most _____ president was John F. Kennedy, at forty-three.
ADJECTIVE

Theodore Roosevelt was the youngest _____ to become
NOUN

president, but that was only after the death of William McKinley.

• President Zachary Taylor coined the term "First _____" in 1849
NOUN

when he described Dolley Madison as America's _____ Lady.
ADJECTIVE

MAD LIBS® is fun to play with friends, but you can also play it by yourself! To begin with, DO NOT look at the story on the page below. Fill in the blanks on this page with the words called for. Then, using the words you have selected, fill in the blank spaces in the story.

Now you've created your own hilarious MAD LIBS® game!

BEST SELLERS FOR KIDS

ADJECTIVE _____

PLURAL NOUN _____

ADJECTIVE _____

NOUN _____

NOUN _____

NOUN _____

NUMBER _____

NUMBER _____

ADJECTIVE _____

NOUN _____

PLURAL NOUN _____

TYPE OF FOOD _____

PLURAL NOUN _____

PLURAL NOUN _____

NOUN _____

ADJECTIVE _____

MAD LIBS

BEST SELLERS FOR KIDS

All children have _____ memories of the books their
　　　　　　　　　ADJECTIVE

mothers and _____ read to them. Here are some of the all-
　　　　　　PLURAL NOUN

time _____ favorites:
　　　ADJECTIVE

• *The Giving* _____ is a touching story about a friendship
　　　　　　　NOUN

between a/an _____ and a tree. Throughout the boy's
　　　　　　NOUN

life, the _____ gives and gives. Kids between the ages of
　　　　NOUN

_____ and _____ love this story.
　NUMBER　　　　　　NUMBER

• *Goodnight Moon* is a/an _____ book that captures
　　　　　　　　　　　　ADJECTIVE

a child's nightly ritual of saying good night to everything in his

_____. It's great for _____ ages two through six.
　NOUN　　　　　　　　　PLURAL NOUN

• Written in rhyme, *Green Eggs and* _____ made Dr. Seuss
　　　　　　　　　　　　　　　　TYPE OF FOOD

one of the best-loved children's _____ of all time. While
　　　　　　　　　　　　　PLURAL NOUN

many _____ have a moral or a/an _____, the lesson
　　PLURAL NOUN　　　　　　　　　NOUN

in this classic is: If you've never tried something, you can't say you

don't like it. A perfect read for all _____ kindergartners.
　　　　　　　　　　　　　　ADJECTIVE

From AD LIB MAD LIBS® • Copyright © 2011 by Price Stern Sloan,
an imprint of Penguin Random House LLC, 345 Hudson Street, New York, NY 10014.

MAD LIBS® is fun to play with friends, but you can also play it by yourself! To begin with, DO NOT look at the story on the page below. Fill in the blanks on this page with the words called for. Then, using the words you have selected, fill in the blank spaces in the story.

Now you've created your own hilarious MAD LIBS® game!

GOOD NIGHT, TEXT

PERSON IN ROOM _____

PERSON IN ROOM _____

ADJECTIVE _____

ADJECTIVE _____

VERB _____

NUMBER _____

PART OF THE BODY (PLURAL) _____

PART OF THE BODY _____

PLURAL NOUN _____

NUMBER _____

NOUN _____

NOUN _____

PLURAL NOUN _____

NOUN _____

ADJECTIVE _____

NOUN _____

MAD LIBS

GOOD NIGHT, TEXT

To be read by _____ and _____:
PERSON IN ROOM   PERSON IN ROOM

PERSON 1: R U awake? Sorry to text you at this _____
ADJECTIVE

hour, but I'm having a/an _____ time trying to _____
ADJECTIVE   VERB

asleep. I've been up for at least _____ hours. And I usually fall
NUMBER

asleep the minute I close my _____.
PART OF THE BODY (PLURAL)

PERSON 2: ? 4U: Do you have something on UR _____?
PART OF THE BODY

PERSON 1: No, I'm just worried I'm never going to fall asleep. I even

tried counting _____. I got to _____
PLURAL NOUN   NUMBER

before I threw in the _____.
NOUN

PERSON 2: RU worried about the _____ test tomorrow?
NOUN

PERSON 1: Nope. I've been cracking the _____ all week.
PLURAL NOUN

PERSON 2: Why don't you drink another _____ of
NOUN

_____ milk?
ADJECTIVE

PERSON 1: It never works. That's an old wives' _____.
NOUN

PERSON 2: What?

PERSON 1: Zzzzzzzzzzzzz.

PERSON 2: Okay, forget the milk.

MAD LIBS® is fun to play with friends, but you can also play it by yourself! To begin with, DO NOT look at the story on the page below. Fill in the blanks on this page with the words called for. Then, using the words you have selected, fill in the blank spaces in the story.

Now you've created your own hilarious MAD LIBS® game!

UNFORGETTABLE BIRTHDAYS

PART OF THE BODY _____

NOUN _____

PLURAL NOUN _____

NOUN _____

ADJECTIVE _____

NOUN _____

ADJECTIVE _____

NOUN _____

PLURAL NOUN _____

NOUN _____

ADJECTIVE _____

VERB ENDING IN "ING" _____

• You're one! A/An _____-opening birthday. A

PART OF THE BODY

birthday you can count on the finger of one _____.

NOUN

You won't remember it, but it is certainly a day to be celebrated by

proud and loving _____.

PLURAL NOUN

• You're five! School days begin. You can attend a public _____

NOUN

and start your _____ education.

ADJECTIVE

• You're thirteen! You are officially a/an _____-ager. The

NOUN

teen years are always a mixture of good, bad, and _____

ADJECTIVE

for you and your parents.

• You're sixteen! You can finally get your driver's _____.

NOUN

But not until you pass the written and the driving _____.

PLURAL NOUN

• You're eighteen! It's cap and _____ time as you graduate

NOUN

from _____ school! Congratulations!

ADJECTIVE

• You're twenty-one! You are now ready to start thinking and

_____ like an adult. Sorry!

VERB ENDING IN "ING"

MAD LIBS® is fun to play with friends, but you can also play it by yourself! To begin with, DO NOT look at the story on the page below. Fill in the blanks on this page with the words called for. Then, using the words you have selected, fill in the blank spaces in the story.

Now you've created your own hilarious MAD LIBS® game!

REMEMBERING NURSERY RHYMES

NOUN _____

PART OF THE BODY _____

ADJECTIVE _____

ADJECTIVE _____

NOUN _____

NOUN _____

ADJECTIVE _____

NOUN _____

NOUN _____

NOUN _____

NOUN _____

ADJECTIVE _____

NOUN _____

NOUN _____

NOUN _____

VERB (PAST TENSE) _____

NOUN _____

NOUN _____

MAD LIBS®
REMEMBERING
NURSERY RHYMES

Memory experts say that once you learn a nursery _____,
NOUN

it stays in your _____ forever. Here are some of the
PART OF THE BODY

most remembered:

• _____ Mother Hubbard went to the cupboard to fetch
ADJECTIVE

her _____ dog a bone; but when she came there, the
ADJECTIVE

_____ was bare, and so the poor _____ had none.
NOUN   NOUN

• _____ Boy Blue, come blow your horn! The _____'s
ADJECTIVE   NOUN

in the meadow, the _____'s in the corn. And where is
NOUN

the _____ who looks after the sheep? He's under the
NOUN

_____, fast asleep.
NOUN

• Mary had a/an _____ lamb, its _____ was white
ADJECTIVE   NOUN

as snow; and everywhere that Mary went, the _____ was
NOUN

sure to go.

• Hey diddle, diddle, the _____ and the fiddle, the cow
NOUN

_____ over the moon. The little dog laughed to see such
VERB (PAST TENSE)

_____, while the dish ran away with the _____.
NOUN   NOUN

MAD LIBS® is fun to play with friends, but you can also play it by yourself! To begin with, DO NOT look at the story on the page below. Fill in the blanks on this page with the words called for. Then, using the words you have selected, fill in the blank spaces in the story.

Now you've created your own hilarious MAD LIBS® game!

GETTING TO KNOW GRANDPA

ADJECTIVE _____

PLURAL NOUN _____

PLURAL NOUN _____

NOUN _____

ADJECTIVE _____

NOUN _____

PLURAL NOUN _____

VERB (PAST TENSE) _____

NOUN _____

PART OF THE BODY (PLURAL) _____

ADJECTIVE _____

ADJECTIVE _____

ADJECTIVE _____

PART OF THE BODY _____

ADJECTIVE _____

NOUN _____

NOUN _____

PLURAL NOUN _____

ADJECTIVE _____

MAD LIBS®
GETTING TO KNOW GRANDPA

I read a/an _____ article in the *New York* _____
                    ADJECTIVE   PLURAL NOUN

about how little most of us know about our grand-_____.
                                                      PLURAL NOUN

So I decided to take the _____ by the horns and spend
                               NOUN

a/an _____ afternoon walking through the _____
          ADJECTIVE   NOUN

orchard with my Grandpa Drew. I learned more in a couple of

_____ than I had in all our previous time together. As we
PLURAL NOUN

_____, I realized what a handsome _____
VERB (PAST TENSE)   NOUN

my grandfather is. He has penetrating blue _____,
                                               PART OF THE BODY (PLURAL)

a/an _____ jaw, and the _____ ability to smile
          ADJECTIVE   ADJECTIVE

you into a good mood in no time. At his _____ age, he
                                             ADJECTIVE

still has a full _____ of hair. But his life has not always
                 PART OF THE BODY

been easy. At a very _____ age, he worked from dusk to
                          ADJECTIVE

_____ to put a/an _____ over his family's head
     NOUN   NOUN

and food on their _____. And he always did it with the
                       PLURAL NOUN

same _____ smile he has today.
          ADJECTIVE

MAD LIBS® is fun to play with friends, but you can also play it by yourself! To begin with, DO NOT look at the story on the page below. Fill in the blanks on this page with the words called for. Then, using the words you have selected, fill in the blank spaces in the story.

Now you've created your own hilarious MAD LIBS® game!

FREE THROWS

PLURAL NOUN _____

ADJECTIVE _____

ADJECTIVE _____

NOUN _____

NOUN _____

NOUN _____

PLURAL NOUN _____

PLURAL NOUN _____

NOUN _____

NUMBER _____

PLURAL NOUN _____

PLURAL NOUN _____

MAD LIBS

FREE THROWS

In pro basketball, free _____ or foul shots are unopposed
PLURAL NOUN

attempts to score points after a/an _____ official calls
ADJECTIVE

a foul on the opposing team. _____ throws are awarded
ADJECTIVE

in many ways. The most common is when a/an _____
NOUN

is fouled in the act of shooting a/an _____. If the foul
NOUN

causes the player to miss the _____, that player is given
NOUN

two or three free _____, depending on where the player
PLURAL NOUN

was when the shot was attempted. If the player makes the shot, the

number of free _____ is reduced to one. The next most
PLURAL NOUN

common form of free throws happens when a/an _____
NOUN

commits more than _____ fouls in one half of the game.
NUMBER

Many basketball _____ are won and lost by the free
PLURAL NOUN

_____ that are made or missed!
PLURAL NOUN

From AD LIB MAD LIBS® • Copyright © 2011 by Price Stern Sloan,
an imprint of Penguin Random House LLC, 345 Hudson Street, New York, NY 10014.

MAD LIBS® is fun to play with friends, but you can also play it by yourself! To begin with, DO NOT look at the story on the page below. Fill in the blanks on this page with the words called for. Then, using the words you have selected, fill in the blank spaces in the story.

Now you've created your own hilarious MAD LIBS® game!

THE NEW ARRIVAL

ADJECTIVE _____

PLURAL NOUN _____

ADJECTIVE _____

NOUN _____

NOUN _____

ADJECTIVE _____

PLURAL NOUN _____

NOUN _____

ADJECTIVE _____

ADJECTIVE _____

NOUN _____

NOUN _____

PLURAL NOUN _____

NOUN _____

ADJECTIVE _____

NOUN _____

ADJECTIVE _____

NOUN _____

MAD☺LIBS®

THE NEW ARRIVAL

One of the most _____ experiences of a young
                         ADJECTIVE

_____'s life is the arrival of a/an _____
    PLURAL NOUN   ADJECTIVE

puppy. The new _____ will immediately become the
                        NOUN

_____ of attention for the _____ family. But it
        NOUN   ADJECTIVE

won't be all fun and _____. Owning a/an _____
                          PLURAL NOUN   NOUN

requires a lot of _____ work and many _____
                        ADJECTIVE   ADJECTIVE

nights. Some owners are surprised when their new _____
                                                            NOUN

acts like the _____ that it is. It will chew the _____,
                    NOUN   PLURAL NOUN

dig up the front _____, and often make its owners feel
                        NOUN

very _____. But they will love the little _____,
          ADJECTIVE   NOUN

anyway, and before long they will watch the _____ pup
                                                      ADJECTIVE

grow into a full-fledged _____.
                               NOUN

MAD LIBS® is fun to play with friends, but you can also play it by yourself! To begin with, DO NOT look at the story on the page below. Fill in the blanks on this page with the words called for. Then, using the words you have selected, fill in the blank spaces in the story.

Now you've created your own hilarious MAD LIBS® game!

UNREAL REALITY

PERSON IN ROOM _____

NOUN _____

COLOR _____

PLURAL NOUN _____

ADJECTIVE _____

ADJECTIVE _____

NOUN _____

NOUN _____

LAST NAME _____

ADJECTIVE _____

ADJECTIVE _____

NUMBER _____

EXCLAMATION _____

ADJECTIVE _____

PLURAL NOUN _____

NOUN _____

NOUN _____

NOUN _____

PLURAL NOUN _____

MAD LIBS
UNREAL REALITY

Television used to be filled with heartwarming family shows like

I Love _____ and *The Brady* _____. Or police
　　　　　PERSON IN ROOM　　　　　　　　　　　　NOUN

shows like *NYPD* _____. But now the airwaves are
　　　　　　　　　　COLOR

loaded with shows called "reality _____," which star
　　　　　　　　　　　　　　　　PLURAL NOUN

_____ people in real-life situations. The audience
ADJECTIVE

follows these _____ celebrities through every minute
　　　　　　　　ADJECTIVE

of their lives—from their _____-cleaning at the
　　　　　　　　　　　　　　NOUN

dentist to their _____-shopping trips to Abercrombie and
　　　　　　　　NOUN

_____. The dating shows are just as _____.
LAST NAME　　　　　　　　　　　　　　　　　ADJECTIVE

One _____ guy meets _____ women and—
　　　ADJECTIVE　　　　　　　　NUMBER

_____!—do those females' _____ claws come out.
EXCLAMATION　　　　　　　　　　ADJECTIVE

Some of the _____ even try to score a/an _____
　　　　　PLURAL NOUN　　　　　　　　　　　　　　　NOUN

on the first date. A few couples have actually tied the _____
　　　　　　　　　　　　　　　　　　　　　　　　NOUN

and walked down the _____. One thing's for sure: Television
　　　　　　　　　NOUN

_____ are not what they used to be.
PLURAL NOUN

MAD LIBS® is fun to play with friends, but you can also play it by yourself! To begin with, DO NOT look at the story on the page below. Fill in the blanks on this page with the words called for. Then, using the words you have selected, fill in the blank spaces in the story.

Now you've created your own hilarious MAD LIBS® game!

ONLINE DATING

ADJECTIVE _____

NOUN _____

ADJECTIVE _____

NOUN _____

VERB ENDING IN "ING" _____

ADJECTIVE _____

PLURAL NOUN _____

PART OF THE BODY _____

NOUN _____

VERB ENDING IN "ING" _____

ADJECTIVE _____

ADJECTIVE _____

PLURAL NOUN _____

NOUN _____

MAD LIBS®
ONLINE DATING

It may seem strange to look for a/an _____ mate or
ADJECTIVE

future _____ on the Internet, but online dating has
NOUN

become one of the most _____ activities on the World
ADJECTIVE

Wide _____. Online _____ provides
NOUN   VERB ENDING IN "ING"

a/an _____ way to connect with _____ without
ADJECTIVE   PLURAL NOUN

a face-to-_____ meeting. People get to know one another
PART OF THE BODY

by chatting through e-mail or talking on the _____. If
NOUN

you try online _____ and decide to meet someone
VERB ENDING IN "ING"

in person, make sure it's in a/an _____ place, and let
ADJECTIVE

a friend know the _____ location. This is also a great
ADJECTIVE

way for shy _____ to meet. And remember, if the first
PLURAL NOUN

introduction doesn't work out, there are many more profiles all over

the _____.
NOUN

MAD LIBS® is fun to play with friends, but you can also play it by yourself! To begin with, DO NOT look at the story on the page below. Fill in the blanks on this page with the words called for. Then, using the words you have selected, fill in the blank spaces in the story.

Now you've created your own hilarious MAD LIBS® game!

MY BFF

PLURAL NOUN _____

NOUN _____

PART OF THE BODY _____

ADJECTIVE _____

NOUN _____

ADJECTIVE _____

NOUN _____

NOUN _____

PLURAL NOUN _____

NOUN _____

ADJECTIVE _____

NOUN _____

ADJECTIVE _____

PART OF THE BODY _____

PLURAL NOUN _____

NOUN _____

VERB _____

MAD LIBS®
MY BFF

Thanks to social networking _____ like My-_____
                                          PLURAL NOUN   NOUN

and _____-book, everyone now has hundreds of
            PART OF THE BODY

_____ friends. But most people really have only one
    ADJECTIVE

best _____. A BFF is someone you tell your deepest,
          NOUN

most _____ secrets to, knowing they won't tell a single
       ADJECTIVE

_____. You and your best _____ can pass
    NOUN   NOUN

_____ in class and share a hot fudge _____ after
  PLURAL NOUN   NOUN

school. And if your _____ friend wants some advice on the
                  ADJECTIVE

latest _____ in their life, you'll give them the _____
      NOUN   ADJECTIVE

truth. And finally, if you ever need a/an _____ to cry
                           PART OF THE BODY

on, your BFF will be there with a box of _____ and a/an
                             PLURAL NOUN

_____ of hot cocoa. Who could _____ for
    NOUN   VERB

anything more?

From AD LIB MAD LIBS® • Copyright © 2011 by Price Stern Sloan,
an imprint of Penguin Random House LLC, 345 Hudson Street, New York, NY 10014.

MAD LIBS® is fun to play with friends, but you can also play it by yourself! To begin with, DO NOT look at the story on the page below. Fill in the blanks on this page with the words called for. Then, using the words you have selected, fill in the blank spaces in the story.

Now you've created your own hilarious MAD LIBS® game!

SOCIAL NETWORKING

PLURAL NOUN _____

PLURAL NOUN _____

NOUN _____

PART OF THE BODY _____

PLURAL NOUN _____

ADJECTIVE _____

NOUN _____

VERB ENDING IN "ING" _____

PLURAL NOUN _____

ADJECTIVE _____

PLURAL NOUN _____

ADJECTIVE _____

NOUN _____

PERSON IN ROOM _____

ADJECTIVE _____

NOUN _____

ADJECTIVE _____

PLURAL NOUN _____

MAD LIBS®
SOCIAL NETWORKING

Do you remember radio, handwritten letters, and landline

_____—all the technology used by your parents to
     PLURAL NOUN

communicate with their _____? These technologies
                    PLURAL NOUN

are now as old as _____. They've been replaced by
             NOUN

Twitter and _____-book. Twitter is a great way to stay
       PART OF THE BODY

in touch with all your _____ and share _____
            PLURAL NOUN   ADJECTIVE

information about what is happening in your own _____.
                                     NOUN

Just remember to keep it to 140 characters. Facebook is a social

_____ service with more than five hundred million
VERB ENDING IN "ING"

_____. You can create a/an _____ profile,
    PLURAL NOUN   ADJECTIVE

add other _____ as friends, and exchange _____
         PLURAL NOUN   ADJECTIVE

messages. Face-_____ was founded by _____
             NOUN   PERSON IN ROOM

and a few of his _____ college classmates. Social networks
           ADJECTIVE

are popular on the _____ Wide Web, where they have
              NOUN

their own _____ language, such as GTG (got to go),
       ADJECTIVE

LOL (laughing out loud), or XOXO (hugs and _____).
                                       PLURAL NOUN

MAD LIBS® is fun to play with friends, but you can also play it by yourself! To begin with, DO NOT look at the story on the page below. Fill in the blanks on this page with the words called for. Then, using the words you have selected, fill in the blank spaces in the story.

Now you've created your own hilarious MAD LIBS® game!

PAUL REVERE'S RIDE

ADJECTIVE _____

LAST NAME _____

NOUN _____

ADJECTIVE _____

ADJECTIVE _____

PLURAL NOUN _____

SAME PLURAL NOUN _____

NOUN _____

VERB _____

NOUN _____

ADJECTIVE _____

NOUN _____

LAST NAME _____

NOUN _____

NOUN _____

MAD LIBS

PAUL REVERE'S RIDE

As a result of the _____ poem by Henry Wadsworth
                           ADJECTIVE

_____, more Americans know of "the midnight
        LAST NAME

ride of Paul Revere" than they do of the _____ it's
                                                NOUN

written about. There are many _____ misconceptions
                                      ADJECTIVE

about Revere's _____ exploits, but the biggest involves him
                   ADJECTIVE

shouting, "The _____ are coming, the _____
                  PLURAL NOUN   SAME PLURAL NOUN

are coming." Historians point out that this _____ was
                                                   NOUN

top secret and on a need-to-_____ basis. His yelling
                                 VERB

would have alerted the British _____ patrols stationed
                                      NOUN

along the _____ route. Historians also point out that
              ADJECTIVE

there were many _____ riders that night, not just Paul
                     NOUN

_____. In any case, historically speaking, you can
        LAST NAME

take Longfellow's "Paul Revere's _____" with a large grain
                                       NOUN

of _____.
      NOUN

MAD LIBS® is fun to play with friends, but you can also play it by yourself! To begin with, DO NOT look at the story on the page below. Fill in the blanks on this page with the words called for. Then, using the words you have selected, fill in the blank spaces in the story.

Now you've created your own hilarious MAD LIBS® game!

GREEN IS GOOD

PLURAL NOUN _____

NOUN _____

NOUN _____

ADJECTIVE _____

PLURAL NOUN _____

PLURAL NOUN _____

PLURAL NOUN _____

TYPE OF LIQUID _____

NOUN _____

NUMBER _____

NOUN _____

ADJECTIVE _____

ADJECTIVE _____

NOUN _____

NOUN _____

PLURAL NOUN _____

MAD LIBS®
GREEN IS GOOD

The era of gas-guzzling _____ is finally coming to a/an
                              PLURAL NOUN

_____. Today, there are many electric cars on the
        NOUN

_____, and more are being developed every day. _____
     NOUN   ADJECTIVE

cars not only reduce greenhouse _____—they also
                                     PLURAL NOUN

dramatically lower our dependence on foreign _____.
                                                  PLURAL NOUN

Many of the new _____ have hybrid batteries, and some
                   PLURAL NOUN

use no _____ at all. Eventually, _____ cars will
         TYPE OF LIQUID   NOUN

go over _____ miles on one _____ of gas. But
           NUMBER   NOUN

the best part of this _____ news is that we will all be
                          ADJECTIVE

breathing more _____ air as the green _____
                  ADJECTIVE   NOUN

grows. So get ready to plug in your _____ charger and
                                         NOUN

see how many _____ you can get per volt!
                 PLURAL NOUN

From AD LIB MAD LIBS® • Copyright © 2011 by Price Stern Sloan,
an imprint of Penguin Random House LLC, 345 Hudson Street, New York, NY 10014.

MAD LIBS® is fun to play with friends, but you can also play it by yourself! To begin with, DO NOT look at the story on the page below. Fill in the blanks on this page with the words called for. Then, using the words you have selected, fill in the blank spaces in the story.

Now you've created your own hilarious MAD LIBS® game!

VIDEO GAMES

PLURAL NOUN _____

NUMBER _____

ADJECTIVE _____

PLURAL NOUN _____

NOUN _____

ADJECTIVE _____

PLURAL NOUN _____

PLURAL NOUN _____

NOUN _____

NOUN _____

A PLACE _____

ADJECTIVE _____

PLURAL NOUN _____

NOUN _____

PLURAL NOUN _____

NOUN _____

MAD☺LIBS®
VIDEO GAMES

Although video _____ have been around for over

_____ years, they've become more and more _____

NUMBER · ADJECTIVE

as developers create more sophisticated _____. Today's

PLURAL NOUN

_____ games are so complicated, they require really

NOUN

_____ attention at all times. They have you sitting

ADJECTIVE

on pins and _____ throughout the entire game. Such

PLURAL NOUN

_____ as *Final* _____ *XIII, Grand Theft*

PLURAL NOUN · NOUN

_____, and *(the)* _____ *Noire* cost more

NOUN · A PLACE

to develop than many _____ movies produced by big

ADJECTIVE

Hollywood _____. If the technology in the video-gaming

PLURAL NOUN

_____ continues to advance, imagine what future electronic

NOUN

_____ will be like. It's _____-boggling.

PLURAL NOUN · NOUN

(PLURAL NOUN under first blank)

From AD LIB MAD LIBS® • Copyright © 2011 by Price Stern Sloan,
an imprint of Penguin Random House LLC, 345 Hudson Street, New York, NY 10014.

MAD LIBS® is fun to play with friends, but you can also play it by yourself! To begin with, DO NOT look at the story on the page below. Fill in the blanks on this page with the words called for. Then, using the words you have selected, fill in the blank spaces in the story.

Now you've created your own hilarious MAD LIBS® game!

THE GREAT AMERICAN PASTIME

ADJECTIVE _____

PLURAL NOUN _____

ADJECTIVE _____

ADJECTIVE _____

NOUN _____

PLURAL NOUN _____

NOUN _____

ADJECTIVE _____

NOUN _____

NOUN _____

PLURAL NOUN _____

ADJECTIVE _____

PART OF THE BODY (PLURAL) _____

ADJECTIVE _____

ADJECTIVE _____

ADJECTIVE _____

NOUN _____

MAD◉LIBS®
THE GREAT
AMERICAN PASTIME

One of the things most _____ sports fans look

ADJECTIVE

forward to at American baseball _____ is eating a/an

PLURAL NOUN

_____ hot dog. There is nothing more traditional

ADJECTIVE

than watching a/an _____ ball game and eating a hot

ADJECTIVE

_____ drenched in mustard, relish, and _____.

NOUN   PLURAL NOUN

Some _____-parks even have their own _____

NOUN   ADJECTIVE

specialties, such as the Dodger _____ in Los Angeles.

NOUN

(It's an oversize steamed or grilled _____.)

NOUN

Hot _____ were created at the end of the nineteenth

PLURAL NOUN

century when a sausage-maker saw his _____ customers

ADJECTIVE

wearing gloves on their _____ because the

PART OF THE BODY (PLURAL)

steaming sausages were too _____ to handle. He put

ADJECTIVE

them in a/an _____ roll, and that was the beginning

ADJECTIVE

of the _____ dog in a bun. The rest, as they say, is

ADJECTIVE

_____!

NOUN

From AD LIB MAD LIBS® • Copyright © 2011 by Price Stern Sloan,
an imprint of Penguin Random House LLC, 345 Hudson Street, New York, NY 10014.

MAD LIBS® is fun to play with friends, but you can also play it by yourself! To begin with, DO NOT look at the story on the page below. Fill in the blanks on this page with the words called for. Then, using the words you have selected, fill in the blank spaces in the story.

Now you've created your own hilarious MAD LIBS® game!

SO YOU WANT TO GET PUBLISHED?

ADJECTIVE _____

ADJECTIVE _____

NOUN _____

NOUN _____

NOUN _____

PART OF THE BODY _____

NOUN _____

NUMBER _____

NOUN _____

VERB ENDING IN "ING" _____

ADJECTIVE _____

NUMBER _____

NOUN _____

PLURAL NOUN _____

PLURAL NOUN _____

ADVERB _____

NOUN _____

ADJECTIVE _____

NOUN _____

MAD LIBS®
SO YOU WANT TO GET PUBLISHED?

As any _____ writer will tell you, writing a book
         ADJECTIVE

is very _____ work. Every author's goal is to
        ADJECTIVE

have a book on the *New York Times* Best _____ List.
                                              NOUN

But it's a long and winding _____ before you hold a
                               NOUN

finished _____ in your _____. Before
            NOUN   PART OF THE BODY

a/an _____ is published, the author can often spend
        NOUN

_____ years writing draft after _____ until it's
  NUMBER   NOUN

ready for _____. Then, a/an _____ editor can
          VERB ENDING IN "ING"   ADJECTIVE

take another _____ months going over the manuscript.
                NUMBER

Finally, the _____ is printed and publicity _____ are
                NOUN   PLURAL NOUN

sent to newspapers, radio stations, and TV _____ across
                                              PLURAL NOUN

the country. Then comes the most exciting part for an author—

seeing the book _____ displayed in _____-stores.
                   ADVERB   NOUN

Of course, today, you can skip this whole _____ process
                                             ADJECTIVE

and self-publish your _____ online.
                         NOUN

MAD LIBS® is fun to play with friends, but you can also play it by yourself! To begin with, DO NOT look at the story on the page below. Fill in the blanks on this page with the words called for. Then, using the words you have selected, fill in the blank spaces in the story.

Now you've created your own hilarious MAD LIBS® game!

MY HIGH-TECH WORLD

NOUN _____

NOUN _____

NOUN _____

NOUN _____

NOUN _____

PLURAL NOUN _____

PLURAL NOUN _____

NOUN _____

VERB ENDING IN "ING" _____

NOUN _____

NOUN _____

NUMBER _____

PLURAL NOUN _____

NOUN _____

ADJECTIVE _____

ADJECTIVE _____

MAD LIBS®

MY HIGH-TECH WORLD

Wow! I bought a new smart-_____ today. It not only
                              NOUN

makes _____ calls—it also forecasts the _____
          NOUN   NOUN

so I know whether to wear a/an _____ or carry a/an
                                      NOUN

_____ in case it rains cats and _____.
        NOUN   PLURAL NOUN

It can also read and send e-_____ and even record a
                              PLURAL NOUN

TV _____. And I will never get lost again because I
      NOUN

now have a global _____ system that gets me from
                    VERB ENDING IN "ING"

point A to _____ B in no time. I also received a/an
                NOUN

_____-reader for my birthday. Imagine not only being
      NOUN

able to download any book in just _____ seconds but
                                      NUMBER

view hundreds of magazines and _____ from all
                                    PLURAL NOUN

over the _____. How did we ever get through each
              NOUN

_____ day before these _____ inventions?
    ADJECTIVE   ADJECTIVE

MAD LIBS® is fun to play with friends, but you can also play it by yourself! To begin with, DO NOT look at the story on the page below. Fill in the blanks on this page with the words called for. Then, using the words you have selected, fill in the blank spaces in the story.

Now you've created your own hilarious MAD LIBS® game!

VAMPIRES AND WEREWOLVES

PLURAL NOUN _____

ADJECTIVE _____

PLURAL NOUN _____

PLURAL NOUN _____

ADJECTIVE _____

ADJECTIVE _____

NOUN _____

NOUN _____

PLURAL NOUN _____

PERSON IN ROOM _____

NOUN _____

PLURAL NOUN _____

NOUN _____

PERSON IN ROOM _____

NUMBER _____

NOUN _____

ADJECTIVE _____

A PLACE _____

MAD LIBS®
VAMPIRES AND WEREWOLVES

Vampires and were-_____ have had a/an _____
        PLURAL NOUN   ADJECTIVE

following for many _____. Books, television _____,
                        PLURAL NOUN   PLURAL NOUN

and movies have all featured these _____ creatures.
                                            ADJECTIVE

Here are some _____ favorites.
                    ADJECTIVE

• *An American* _____ *in London* is a horror/comedy
                        NOUN

_____ about two _____ who are attacked by a
      NOUN   PLURAL NOUN

British werewolf.

• _____ *the Vampire Slayer* is a TV show that
      PERSON IN ROOM

follows a young _____ who fights against demons
                        NOUN

and other _____ of darkness.
                PLURAL NOUN

• *The Twilight Saga* is about a teenage _____ named
                                                NOUN

_____ who falls in love with a/an _____-year-
    PERSON IN ROOM   NUMBER

old vampire.

• *True* _____ is a television series in which vampires
            NOUN

try to be _____ citizens in a small town in (the)
                ADJECTIVE

_____.
    A PLACE

From AD LIB MAD LIBS® • Copyright © 2011 by Price Stern Sloan,
an imprint of Penguin Random House LLC, 345 Hudson Street, New York, NY 10014.

MAD LIBS® is fun to play with friends, but you can also play it by yourself! To begin with, DO NOT look at the story on the page below. Fill in the blanks on this page with the words called for. Then, using the words you have selected, fill in the blank spaces in the story.

Now you've created your own hilarious MAD LIBS® game!

RUN, RUN, RUN

PLURAL NOUN _____

ADJECTIVE _____

NUMBER _____

PART OF THE BODY (PLURAL) _____

NOUN _____

VERB ENDING IN "ING" _____

ADJECTIVE _____

ADJECTIVE _____

NOUN _____

PLURAL NOUN _____

VERB ENDING IN "ING" _____

ADJECTIVE _____

NOUN _____

NOUN _____

NOUN _____

ADJECTIVE _____

ADJECTIVE _____

MAD LIBS

RUN, RUN, RUN

If your streets are suddenly packed like _____, you
can assume it's either a/an _____ parade or a marathon.

The marathon, a/an _____-mile race, has captured the hearts

and _____ of runners around the _____.

More people are _____ than ever before. So if you're

attracted to this _____ idea, here's a/an _____

way to train for a marathon and have fun while doing it. The secret

to running is training every _____ and eating delicious

and nutritious _____. The days of _____

till you drop are long gone. Today, it takes a lot more than good old

_____ determination and _____ power. To run

a marathon, you have to rely on the _____ of your mind.

Once the mind takes over, you cannot allow the _____ to

tell it what to do. Now, go buy some _____ sneakers, and

good luck on your _____ marathon.

From AD LIB MAD LIBS® • Copyright © 2011 by Price Stern Sloan,
an imprint of Penguin Random House LLC, 345 Hudson Street, New York, NY 10014.

Join the millions of Mad Libs fans
creating wacky and wonderful
stories on our apps!

Download Mad Libs today!

MAD ABOUT ANIMALS
MAD LIBS

By Roger Price and Leonard Stern

PSS!
PRICE STERN SLOAN
An Imprint of Penguin Random House

MAD☺LIBS
INSTRUCTIONS

MAD LIBS® is a game for people who don't like games!
It can be played by one, two, three, four, or forty.

• RIDICULOUSLY SIMPLE DIRECTIONS

In this tablet you will find stories containing blank spaces where words
are left out. One player, the READER, selects one of these stories. The
READER does not tell anyone what the story is about. Instead, he/she asks
the other players, the WRITERS, to give him/her words. These words are
used to fill in the blank spaces in the story.

• TO PLAY

The READER asks each WRITER in turn to call out a word—an adjective or
a noun or whatever the space calls for—and uses them to fill in the blank
spaces in the story. The result is a MAD LIBS® game.

When the READER then reads the completed MAD LIBS® game to the other
players, they will discover that they have written a story that is fantastic,
screamingly funny, shocking, silly, crazy, or just plain dumb—depending
upon which words each WRITER called out.

• EXAMPLE (*Before* and *After*)

"_____!" he said _____
　　　　　EXCLAMATION　　　　　　　　　　　　ADVERB

as he jumped into his convertible _____ and
　　　　　　　　　　　　　　　　　　　　NOUN

drove off with his _____ wife.
　　　　　　　　ADJECTIVE

"___*Ouch*___!" he said ___*stupidly*___
　　　EXCLAMATION　　　　　　　　　ADVERB

as he jumped into his convertible ___*cat*___ and
　　　　　　　　　　　　　　　NOUN

drove off with his ___*brave*___ wife.
　　　　　　　ADJECTIVE

In case you have forgotten what adjectives, adverbs, nouns, and verbs are, here is a quick review:

An ADJECTIVE describes something or somebody. *Lumpy*, *soft*, *ugly*, *messy*, and *short* are adjectives.

An ADVERB tells how something is done. It modifies a verb and usually ends in "ly." *Modestly*, *stupidly*, *greedily*, and *carefully* are adverbs.

A NOUN is the name of a person, place, or thing. *Sidewalk*, *umbrella*, *bridle*, *bathtub*, and *nose* are nouns.

A VERB is an action word. *Run*, *pitch*, *jump*, and *swim* are verbs. Put the verbs in past tense if the directions say PAST TENSE. *Ran*, *pitched*, *jumped*, and *swam* are verbs in the past tense.

When we ask for A PLACE, we mean any sort of place: a country or city (*Spain*, *Cleveland*) or a room (*bathroom*, *kitchen*).

An EXCLAMATION or SILLY WORD is any sort of funny sound, gasp, grunt, or outcry, like *Wow!*, *Ouch!*, *Whomp!*, *Ick!*, and *Gadzooks!*

When we ask for specific words, like a NUMBER, a COLOR, an ANIMAL, or a PART OF THE BODY, we mean a word that is one of those things, like *seven*, *blue*, *horse*, or *head*.

When we ask for a PLURAL, it means more than one. For example, *cat* pluralized is *cats*.

MAD LIBS® is fun to play with friends, but you can also play it by yourself! To begin with, DO NOT look at the story on the page below. Fill in the blanks on this page with the words called for. Then, using the words you have selected, fill in the blank spaces in the story.

Now you've created your own hilarious MAD LIBS® game!

DOG'S POINT OF VIEW

PERSON IN ROOM (MALE) _____

PART OF THE BODY (PLURAL) _____

NOUN _____

PART OF THE BODY _____

ADJECTIVE _____

ADVERB _____

NOUN _____

ADJECTIVE _____

ADJECTIVE _____

PART OF THE BODY _____

PART OF THE BODY (PLURAL) _____

ADJECTIVE _____

PLURAL NOUN _____

PLURAL NOUN _____

VERB _____

ADJECTIVE _____

NOUN _____

ADJECTIVE _____

NOUN _____

MAD LIBS®

DOG'S POINT OF VIEW

The minute I saw _____ pucker his _____
PERSON IN ROOM (MALE)   PART OF THE BODY (PLURAL)

and whistle, I knew we were going for a/an _____
NOUN

ride. I wagged my _____, gave a/an _____
PART OF THE BODY   ADJECTIVE

bark, and _____ leaped into the back- _____
ADVERB   NOUN

of the car. As we began our _____ drive through the
ADJECTIVE

_____ neighborhood, I stuck my _____
ADJECTIVE   PART OF THE BODY

out the window, felt the wind in my _____,
PART OF THE BODY (PLURAL)

and took in all the _____ smells. We drove past cars,
ADJECTIVE

people, and _____. Then it hit me like a ton of
PLURAL NOUN

_____—we were headed for the dog park! I'd get to
PLURAL NOUN

see and _____ with my _____ girlfriend,
VERB   ADJECTIVE

Fifi, who is a purebred French _____. Yes, sir, despite
NOUN

all the _____ publicity, there's nothing like a dog's life
ADJECTIVE

when you have a generous and caring _____ like mine.
NOUN

MAD LIBS® is fun to play with friends, but you can also play it by yourself! To begin with, DO NOT look at the story on the page below. Fill in the blanks on this page with the words called for. Then, using the words you have selected, fill in the blank spaces in the story.

Now you've created your own hilarious MAD LIBS® game!

POSTCARD FROM A SAFARI

ADJECTIVE _____

ADJECTIVE _____

PLURAL NOUN _____

NOUN _____

PLURAL NOUN _____

TYPE OF LIQUID _____

ADJECTIVE _____

A PLACE _____

NOUN _____

NOUN _____

NOUN _____

PART OF THE BODY _____

ADJECTIVE _____

ADJECTIVE _____

NUMBER _____

NOUN _____

VERB ENDING IN "ING" _____

MAD LIBS®

POSTCARD FROM A SAFARI

Wish you were here on this _____ African safari!
                              ADJECTIVE

We are having the most _____ time of our
                              ADJECTIVE

_____. Believe it or not, on the first day, we saw a
PLURAL NOUN

mother _____ and her baby _____
              NOUN   PLURAL NOUN

drinking _____ from a watering hole. The second
              TYPE OF LIQUID

day, we climbed onto the back of a/an _____
                                              ADJECTIVE

elephant and went through (the) _____, and the
                                      A PLACE

beauty took my _____ away. But the best—and
                      NOUN

weirdest—part was saved for last. We were deep in the forest

when a huge _____ climbed onto the hood of our
                  NOUN

_____ and took a swipe at us with its powerful
NOUN

_____. But as this letter attests, we survived. All in
PART OF THE BODY

all, this has been a really _____ trip. Thankfully you'll
                                  ADJECTIVE

be able to share our _____ adventures because I've
                          ADJECTIVE

taken more than _____ pictures with my trusty digital
                      NUMBER

_____. As they say, seeing is _____!
NOUN   VERB ENDING IN "ING"

MAD LIBS® is fun to play with friends, but you can also play it by yourself! To begin with, DO NOT look at the story on the page below. Fill in the blanks on this page with the words called for. Then, using the words you have selected, fill in the blank spaces in the story.

Now you've created your own hilarious MAD LIBS® game!

AUSTRALIAN WILDLIFE

NOUN _____

ADJECTIVE _____

NOUN _____

PART OF THE BODY (PLURAL) _____

NOUN _____

ADJECTIVE _____

PLURAL NOUN _____

PLURAL NOUN _____

PLURAL NOUN _____

NOUN _____

PLURAL NOUN _____

NOUN _____

NOUN _____

PLURAL NOUN _____

ADJECTIVE _____

AUSTRALIAN WILDLIFE

Australia, also known as the _____ Down Under,
NOUN

is famous for its _____ wildlife. The most
ADJECTIVE

famous animal is the kangaroo, which carries its baby in a/an

_____ on its belly and travels by hopping on its
NOUN

powerful hind _____. The koala is another popular
PART OF THE BODY (PLURAL)

Australian _____. This furry, _____
NOUN   ADJECTIVE

creature loves to eat leaves from eucalyptus _____. If
PLURAL NOUN

you are a bird-watcher, the emu will knock your _____
PLURAL NOUN

off. It is a bird that has no _____ and cannot fly, but
PLURAL NOUN

it can run faster than a speeding _____. Perhaps the
NOUN

strangest of all Australian _____ is the platypus. It has a
PLURAL NOUN

bill that resembles a duck's _____ and the body of
NOUN

a/an _____. It is one of only two mammals that lay
NOUN

_____ instead of giving birth to their young. If you
PLURAL NOUN

are a nature lover, you must put exotic and _____
ADJECTIVE

Australia on your places-to-go list!

MAD LIBS® is fun to play with friends, but you can also play it by yourself! To begin with, DO NOT look at the story on the page below. Fill in the blanks on this page with the words called for. Then, using the words you have selected, fill in the blank spaces in the story.

Now you've created your own hilarious MAD LIBS® game!

SCHOOL PET FRET

ADJECTIVE _____

PERSON IN ROOM (MALE) _____

ADJECTIVE _____

NOUN _____

NOUN _____

NOUN _____

PART OF THE BODY _____

VERB ENDING IN "ING" _____

ADVERB _____

NUMBER _____

PLURAL NOUN _____

ADJECTIVE _____

ADJECTIVE _____

ADJECTIVE _____

EXCLAMATION _____

PLURAL NOUN _____

MAD LIBS®

SCHOOL PET FRET

I recently had the honor of taking our class pet, a/an _____
ADJECTIVE

rabbit named _____, to my house for the weekend.
PERSON IN ROOM (MALE)

I carried the little guy in his _____ cage and left him
ADJECTIVE

on the kitchen _____ as I went about my afternoon
NOUN

chores of unloading the _____-washer and taking out the
NOUN

_____. When I came back, my _____ dropped
NOUN   PART OF THE BODY

open in shock. He was gone! My heart was _____ a mile
VERB ENDING IN "ING"

a minute as I _____ ran through the house. I checked
ADVERB

every room at least _____ times. Desperate, I even checked
NUMBER

my pile of dirty _____ twice. But I couldn't find him
PLURAL NOUN

anywhere. Finally I heard a/an _____ noise and I followed
ADJECTIVE

it to the basement. There, right next to the _____
ADJECTIVE

water heater, was my classroom's precious rabbit—with five

_____ baby rabbits. _____! The *he* was a *she*!
ADJECTIVE   EXCLAMATION

And she had just given birth to a litter of _____!
PLURAL NOUN

From MAD ABOUT ANIMALS MAD LIBS® • Copyright © 2009 by Price Stern Sloan,
an imprint of Penguin Random House LLC, 345 Hudson Street, New York, NY 10014.

MAD LIBS® is fun to play with friends, but you can also play it by yourself! To begin with, DO NOT look at the story on the page below. Fill in the blanks on this page with the words called for. Then, using the words you have selected, fill in the blank spaces in the story.

Now you've created your own hilarious MAD LIBS® game!

CALLING ALL BIRDS

ADJECTIVE _____

NOUN _____

ADJECTIVE _____

ADJECTIVE _____

NOUN _____

ADJECTIVE _____

PART OF THE BODY _____

NOUN _____

ADJECTIVE _____

PART OF THE BODY _____

NOUN _____

ADJECTIVE _____

NOUN _____

NOUN _____

NOUN _____

MAD LIBS®
CALLING ALL BIRDS

Every bird has a/an _____ song or call—and every
ADJECTIVE

talented _____-watcher knows how to imitate them
NOUN

precisely. The following three _____ birds can be easily
ADJECTIVE

imitated by a/an _____ amateur.
ADJECTIVE

• The yellow-bellied sap _____: A/An _____
NOUN   ADJECTIVE

  member of the woodpecker family, its call can be easily

  reproduced by squeezing your _____ as tightly as
PART OF THE BODY

  possible and meowing like a hungry _____.
NOUN

• The pelican: Its _____ call is easy to repeat, provided
ADJECTIVE

  you stretch your _____ to its fullest length before
PART OF THE BODY

  emitting a squawk-like _____.
NOUN

• The cockatoo: Its vocalization is loud and _____.
ADJECTIVE

  But cockatoos primarily emit a soft, growling _____
NOUN

  when feeding. They also communicate by drumming a dead

  _____ with a stick. And when threatened, they issue
NOUN

  an easily duplicated hissing _____.
NOUN

MAD LIBS® is fun to play with friends, but you can also play it by yourself! To begin with, DO NOT look at the story on the page below. Fill in the blanks on this page with the words called for. Then, using the words you have selected, fill in the blank spaces in the story.

Now you've created your own hilarious MAD LIBS® game!

FIELD TRIP TO THE ZOO

ADJECTIVE _____

ADJECTIVE _____

ADJECTIVE _____

ADJECTIVE _____

ADJECTIVE _____

PLURAL NOUN _____

PLURAL NOUN _____

ADJECTIVE _____

PART OF THE BODY (PLURAL) _____

NOUN _____

ADJECTIVE _____

PLURAL NOUN _____

PLURAL NOUN _____

ADJECTIVE _____

NOUN _____

PART OF THE BODY (PLURAL) _____

PERSON IN ROOM _____

PART OF THE BODY _____

MAD LIBS®
FIELD TRIP TO THE ZOO

Okay, class! Here we are at the _____ zoo. It is a/an
ADJECTIVE

_____ place to enjoy _____ experiences,
ADJECTIVE   ADJECTIVE

but in order to do so, you must obey these _____ rules.
ADJECTIVE

Rule #1 is personal: Have a/an _____ time.
ADJECTIVE

Rule #2: Please don't feed the _____. They eat
PLURAL NOUN

scientifically formulated _____ to ensure they
PLURAL NOUN

remain in _____ health. Human food can upset
ADJECTIVE

their _____ and make them sicker than a/an
PART OF THE BODY (PLURAL)

_____ .
NOUN

Rule #3: Don't litter. Make sure you throw all of your _____
ADJECTIVE

wrappers and plastic _____ into trash _____
PLURAL NOUN   PLURAL NOUN

to keep the zoo sparkling and _____ .
ADJECTIVE

Rule #4: Respect boundaries. When you approach a wild _____
NOUN

cage, keep your _____ to yourself at all times. Last
PART OF THE BODY (PLURAL)

year, _____ attempted to pet an orangutan and almost
PERSON IN ROOM

lost his/her left _____ .
PART OF THE BODY

From MAD ABOUT ANIMALS MAD LIBS® • Copyright © 2009 by Price Stern Sloan,
an imprint of Penguin Random House LLC, 345 Hudson Street, New York, NY 10014.

MAD LIBS® is fun to play with friends, but you can also play it by yourself! To begin with, DO NOT look at the story on the page below. Fill in the blanks on this page with the words called for. Then, using the words you have selected, fill in the blank spaces in the story.

Now you've created your own hilarious MAD LIBS® game!

LEGENDARY CREATURES

ADJECTIVE _____

ADJECTIVE _____

PLURAL NOUN _____

NOUN _____

ADJECTIVE _____

PLURAL NOUN _____

A PLACE _____

ADJECTIVE _____

NOUN _____

PART OF THE BODY _____

NOUN _____

ADJECTIVE _____

ADJECTIVE _____

NOUN _____

PLURAL NOUN _____

PLURAL NOUN _____

ADJECTIVE _____

MAD LIBS®

LEGENDARY CREATURES

Throughout time, man has heard _____ tales of
ADJECTIVE

_____, mythical creatures that challenge the imagination.
ADJECTIVE

Here are the most famous of these _____:
PLURAL NOUN

• The **mermaid**, half human, half _____, was known to
NOUN

sing _____ songs that caused sailors to crash their
ADJECTIVE

_____ in the middle of (the) _____.
PLURAL NOUN   A PLACE

• The **unicorn** was described as a/an _____ horse
ADJECTIVE

with a pointy _____ in the middle of its _____,
NOUN   PART OF THE BODY

a billy-goat beard, a lion's _____, and _____
NOUN   ADJECTIVE

hooves. It was believed to bring _____ luck to those
ADJECTIVE

who were fortunate enough to see it.

• The **griffin** had the body of a/an _____ and the
NOUN

head and _____ of an eagle. Legend has it that they
PLURAL NOUN

guarded treasures of priceless _____. It is also
PLURAL NOUN

believed they had the power to make a/an _____
ADJECTIVE

man see.

From MAD ABOUT ANIMALS MAD LIBS® • Copyright © 2009 by Price Stern Sloan,
an imprint of Penguin Random House LLC, 345 Hudson Street, New York, NY 10014.

MAD LIBS® is fun to play with friends, but you can also play it by yourself! To begin with, DO NOT look at the story on the page below. Fill in the blanks on this page with the words called for. Then, using the words you have selected, fill in the blank spaces in the story.

Now you've created your own hilarious MAD LIBS® game!

CATS VS. DOGS, PART 1

ADJECTIVE _____

ADJECTIVE _____

VERB _____

NOUN _____

PLURAL NOUN _____

NOUN _____

PART OF THE BODY (PLURAL) _____

NOUN _____

ADJECTIVE _____

PART OF THE BODY _____

ADJECTIVE _____

PART OF THE BODY _____

NUMBER _____

MAD LIBS®

CATS VS. DOGS, PART 1

The _____ debate remains: Which pet is better, a cat or a dog?

ADJECTIVE

Here are some *purr*-fect reasons why cats make _____ pets:

ADJECTIVE

• Cats come and _____ as they please, exploring the

VERB

neighbor's _____, climbing tall _____, or

NOUN   PLURAL NOUN

basking in the midday _____.

NOUN

• Cats are mysterious. Take one look into a cat's diamond-shaped

_____, and you're sure it's reading your _____.

PART OF THE BODY (PLURAL)   NOUN

• Cats are known for their _____ cleanliness. They wash

ADJECTIVE

themselves by licking their fur with their scratchy _____.

PART OF THE BODY

• Cats purr. It's a truly _____ sound that can even win

ADJECTIVE

the _____ of a non-cat lover.

PART OF THE BODY

• Finally, a cat is reputed to have _____ lives, which

NUMBER

makes it the cat's meow!

MAD LIBS® is fun to play with friends, but you can also play it by yourself! To begin with, DO NOT look at the story on the page below. Fill in the blanks on this page with the words called for. Then, using the words you have selected, fill in the blank spaces in the story.

Now you've created your own hilarious MAD LIBS® game!

CATS VS. DOGS, PART 2

ADJECTIVE _____

NOUN _____

ADJECTIVE _____

NOUN _____

ADVERB _____

PART OF THE BODY _____

NUMBER _____

NOUN _____

ADJECTIVE _____

ADJECTIVE _____

NUMBER _____

ADJECTIVE _____

ADJECTIVE _____

ADJECTIVE _____

NOUN _____

NOUN _____

NOUN _____

NOUN _____

MAD LIBS®

CATS VS. DOGS, PART 2

Now, from the opposing side—here are a few _____
_____ ADJECTIVE

reasons why dogs are considered man's best _____:
_____ NOUN

• Dogs are _____ companions. They love to play. You can
_____ ADJECTIVE

   throw a rubber _____ and a dog will _____
   _____ NOUN _____ ADVERB

   chase it and carry it back to you in its _____ at least
   _____ PART OF THE BODY

   _____ times.
   NUMBER

• Dogs can keep your _____ safe. Their _____
   _____ NOUN _____ ADJECTIVE

   sense of hearing and _____ sense of smell justify the
   _____ ADJECTIVE

   term *watchdog.*

• There are more than _____ breeds of dogs. You can
   _____ NUMBER

   pick a/an _____ Chihuahua or a/an _____
   _____ ADJECTIVE _____ ADJECTIVE

   Dane, and each will have its own _____ personality.
   _____ ADJECTIVE

• You can't get a more loyal _____ than a dog. Just
   _____ NOUN

   rub a dog's _____ and you will have a/an _____
   _____ NOUN _____ NOUN

   for life.

• And the good news—a dog's bark is usually worse than its _____!
   _____ NOUN

From MAD ABOUT ANIMALS MAD LIBS® • Copyright © 2009 by Price Stern Sloan,
an imprint of Penguin Random House LLC, 345 Hudson Street, New York, NY 10014.

MAD LIBS® is fun to play with friends, but you can also play it by yourself! To begin with, DO NOT look at the story on the page below. Fill in the blanks on this page with the words called for. Then, using the words you have selected, fill in the blank spaces in the story.

Now you've created your own hilarious MAD LIBS® game!

DINO-MITE

ADJECTIVE _____

VERB (PAST TENSE) _____

PERSON IN ROOM _____

ADJECTIVE _____

PART OF THE BODY _____

PLURAL NOUN _____

NOUN _____

PLURAL NOUN _____

ADJECTIVE _____

ADJECTIVE _____

NOUN _____

ADJECTIVE _____

ADJECTIVE _____

PLURAL NOUN _____

NOUN _____

ADJECTIVE _____

TYPE OF LIQUID _____

PLURAL NOUN _____

PLURAL NOUN _____

NOUN _____

MAD LIBS®
DINO-MITE

Millions of years ago, _____ creatures called dinosaurs
ADJECTIVE

_____ all over the earth. The largest was the Tyrannosaurus
VERB (PAST TENSE)

_____. Strangely, this _____ beast had a small
PERSON IN ROOM   ADJECTIVE

_____ and was a scavenger that ate mostly _____.
PART OF THE BODY   PLURAL NOUN

The brontosaurus, an herbivore, had a very long _____,
                                                   NOUN

which helped it reach up and eat _____ from the tops of
                                    PLURAL NOUN

_____ trees. The stegosaurus had _____ scales that
ADJECTIVE   ADJECTIVE

were used as armor when it was attacked by a/an _____,
                                                   NOUN

and it ate a variety of _____ fruits and _____
                          ADJECTIVE   ADJECTIVE

foliage. Unfortunately, dinosaurs disappeared long before human

_____ appeared on earth. What happened to them?
PLURAL NOUN

Scientists think a giant _____ fell from space, creating a/an
                           NOUN

_____ wave of _____ and dust that destroyed these
ADJECTIVE   TYPE OF LIQUID

magnificent _____. Today, archeologists are still digging up
              PLURAL NOUN

dinosaur _____, which can be seen in museums all over the
           PLURAL NOUN

_____.
NOUN

MAD LIBS® is fun to play with friends, but you can also play it by yourself! To begin with, DO NOT look at the story on the page below. Fill in the blanks on this page with the words called for. Then, using the words you have selected, fill in the blank spaces in the story.

Now you've created your own hilarious MAD LIBS® game!

AMAZING DADS

ADJECTIVE _____

PLURAL NOUN _____

PLURAL NOUN _____

ADJECTIVE _____

ADJECTIVE _____

NUMBER _____

ADJECTIVE _____

PLURAL NOUN _____

NOUN _____

PART OF THE BODY _____

ADJECTIVE _____

PLURAL NOUN _____

NOUN _____

ADJECTIVE _____

ADJECTIVE _____

PART OF THE BODY _____

NUMBER _____

ADJECTIVE _____

NOUN _____

MAD LIBS®

AMAZING DADS

You hear a lot about _____ mothers in the wild,
                         ADJECTIVE

nurturing and taking care of their _____. But what most
                                      PLURAL NOUN

_____ don't know is that there are a lot of great animal
   PLURAL NOUN

dads, too. A/An _____ example is the _____
                    ADJECTIVE   ADJECTIVE

sea horse. After a courtship dance of _____ hours, the
                                           NUMBER

female gives her _____ eggs to the male, who carries them
                    ADJECTIVE

until they hatch. Emperor penguins are hands-on _____, too.
                                                     PLURAL NOUN

After the mother lays a/an _____, the dad carries it in his
                                NOUN

_____ to keep it _____ and warm while
 PART OF THE BODY   ADJECTIVE

she goes off to look for _____ to eat. He holds on to the
                             PLURAL NOUN

_____ throughout the cold, _____ winter.
    NOUN   ADJECTIVE

Another example of dad care is the _____ cardinal fish.
                                        ADJECTIVE

After the female fertilizes the eggs, the proud father keeps them in

his _____ for _____ days, until they hatch.
      PART OF THE BODY   NUMBER

Each of these _____ fathers deserves a trophy that says
                    ADJECTIVE

"World's #1 _____!"
                NOUN

From MAD ABOUT ANIMALS MAD LIBS® • Copyright © 2009 by Price Stern Sloan,
an imprint of Penguin Random House LLC, 345 Hudson Street, New York, NY 10014.

MAD LIBS® is fun to play with friends, but you can also play it by yourself! To begin with, DO NOT look at the story on the page below. Fill in the blanks on this page with the words called for. Then, using the words you have selected, fill in the blank spaces in the story.

Now you've created your own hilarious MAD LIBS® game!

PANDAMANIA

PLURAL NOUN _____

ADJECTIVE _____

NOUN _____

ADJECTIVE _____

NOUN _____

VERB ENDING IN "ING" _____

PLURAL NOUN _____

EXCLAMATION _____

PART OF THE BODY (PLURAL) _____

ADJECTIVE _____

PART OF THE BODY (PLURAL) _____

NOUN _____

NOUN _____

NOUN _____

PLURAL NOUN _____

PLURAL NOUN _____

MAD LIBS®
PANDAMANIA

Welcome back to the *World of Wild* _____. When we

PLURAL NOUN

left off, we were tracking the _____ panda in the forests

ADJECTIVE

of China, hoping to catch a glimpse of a newborn _____.

NOUN

Now, we are making our way through the _____

ADJECTIVE

bamboo forest, trying to be as quiet as a/an _____.

NOUN

Wait! Something is _____ behind a bush! We can't

VERB ENDING IN "ING"

see it, so we have to part some thick bamboo _____.

PLURAL NOUN

_____! I can't believe my _____. There

EXCLAMATION   PART OF THE BODY (PLURAL)

is a mother panda, cradling her _____ cub in her

ADJECTIVE

_____. The baby is the size of a miniature

PART OF THE BODY (PLURAL)

_____! It's the most beautiful _____

NOUN   NOUN

I've ever seen. Uh-oh, the mother _____ doesn't

NOUN

look too happy that we're here. Oh my _____, it

PLURAL NOUN

looks like she's coming after us! Run for your _____!

PLURAL NOUN

From MAD ABOUT ANIMALS MAD LIBS® • Copyright © 2009 by Price Stern Sloan,
an imprint of Penguin Random House LLC, 345 Hudson Street, New York, NY 10014.

MAD LIBS® is fun to play with friends, but you can also play it by yourself! To begin with, DO NOT look at the story on the page below. Fill in the blanks on this page with the words called for. Then, using the words you have selected, fill in the blank spaces in the story.

Now you've created your own hilarious MAD LIBS® game!

DOLPHINSPEAK

ADJECTIVE _____

PLURAL NOUN_____

NOUN _____

ADJECTIVE _____

PLURAL NOUN_____

ADJECTIVE _____

ADJECTIVE _____

PLURAL NOUN_____

ADJECTIVE _____

PLURAL NOUN_____

PART OF THE BODY (PLURAL) _____

OCCUPATION_____

ADJECTIVE _____

PERSON IN ROOM _____

ADVERB _____

MAD LIBS®
DOLPHINSPEAK

Humans have many _____ ways of communicating with

ADJECTIVE

one another. Today we depend on TV, cell _____, and

PLURAL NOUN

e-_____ to get our information. Dolphins may not use

NOUN

technology as _____ as ours, but they are highly

ADJECTIVE

advanced _____ with a/an _____ capacity

PLURAL NOUN · · · · ADJECTIVE

for language skills. They communicate by making _____

ADJECTIVE

noises that sound like _____, called sonar. Their

PLURAL NOUN

_____ sounds bounce off underwater _____,

ADJECTIVE · · · · PLURAL NOUN

traveling to the _____ of other dolphins. This

PART OF THE BODY (PLURAL)

makes it easy for dolphins to alert their friends that there's a

deep-sea _____ swimming nearby, or to share the

OCCUPATION

latest _____ gossip about _____. So the

ADJECTIVE · · · · PERSON IN ROOM

next time you're at an aquarium, listen _____

ADVERB

to the dolphins: They might just be talking about you!

MAD LIBS® is fun to play with friends, but you can also play it by yourself! To begin with, DO NOT look at the story on the page below. Fill in the blanks on this page with the words called for. Then, using the words you have selected, fill in the blank spaces in the story.

Now you've created your own hilarious MAD LIBS® game!

IN THE NURSERY, PART 1

ADJECTIVE _____

ADJECTIVE _____

ADJECTIVE _____

ADJECTIVE _____

PLURAL NOUN _____

VERB ENDING IN "ING" _____

ADJECTIVE _____

PLURAL NOUN _____

NOUN _____

NUMBER _____

ADJECTIVE _____

NOUN _____

PLURAL NOUN _____

PLURAL NOUN _____

PLURAL NOUN _____

ADVERB _____

ADJECTIVE _____

NOUN _____

NOUN _____

Most _____ bedtime stories revolve around _____
    ADJECTIVE   ADJECTIVE

animals—and they usually end happily. Here are some _____
                                                                        ADJECTIVE

examples of this theory:

• "The Three _____ Pigs": The pigs build houses made
                    ADJECTIVE

  of straw, sticks, and _____. By huffing and _____,
                              PLURAL NOUN   VERB ENDING IN "ING"

  the big, _____ wolf blows the first two _____
                ADJECTIVE   PLURAL NOUN

  down—but he just can't blow down the brick _____.
                                                                  NOUN

• "Goldilocks and the _____ Bears": While the _____
                            NUMBER   ADJECTIVE

  bears are away, Goldilocks sneaks in their house, eats their

  _____, sits in their _____, and sleeps in
          NOUN   PLURAL NOUN

  their _____. The three _____ come home,
              PLURAL NOUN   PLURAL NOUN

  but Goldilocks _____ escapes.
                        ADVERB

• "The Frog Prince": A/An _____ princess befriends
                                  ADJECTIVE

  a frog, but when she kisses his _____, he transforms
                                            NOUN

  into a handsome _____.
                        NOUN

MAD LIBS® is fun to play with friends, but you can also play it by yourself! To begin with, DO NOT look at the story on the page below. Fill in the blanks on this page with the words called for. Then, using the words you have selected, fill in the blank spaces in the story.

Now you've created your own hilarious MAD LIBS® game!

IN THE NURSERY, PART 2

NOUN _____

NOUN _____

PLURAL NOUN _____

VERB _____

ADJECTIVE _____

NOUN _____

ADJECTIVE _____

ADJECTIVE _____

ADJECTIVE _____

ADJECTIVE _____

PART OF THE BODY (PLURAL) _____

PLURAL NOUN _____

ADJECTIVE _____

PLURAL NOUN _____

NOUN _____

PLURAL NOUN _____

ADJECTIVE _____

ADJECTIVE _____

• "Little Red Riding _____": This story features another
  NOUN

big, bad _____. This wolf disguises himself as Little
         NOUN

Red's grandmother. "My, what big _____ you have!" she
                                   PLURAL NOUN

cries. "The better to _____ you with, my dear," the wolf
                       VERB

replies. Ultimately, Little Red _____ Hood is rescued by
                                 ADJECTIVE

a/an _____.
     NOUN

• "The _____ Duckling": The duckling feels he's
       ADJECTIVE

more _____ than the other ducks. All his friends taunt
     ADJECTIVE

him: "Look how _____ he is! He's not one of us!"
                ADJECTIVE

When he turns into a/an _____ swan, they can't believe
                        ADJECTIVE

their _____.
      PART OF THE BODY (PLURAL)

• "Puss in _____": A/An _____ miller's son
           PLURAL NOUN   ADJECTIVE

inherits a cat who promises him riches and _____ in
                                            PLURAL NOUN

return for a bag containing a/an _____ and a pair
                                 NOUN

of high leather _____. Eventually the _____
                 PLURAL NOUN   ADJECTIVE

son marries a/an _____ princess.
                 ADJECTIVE

MAD LIBS® is fun to play with friends, but you can also play it by yourself! To begin with, DO NOT look at the story on the page below. Fill in the blanks on this page with the words called for. Then, using the words you have selected, fill in the blank spaces in the story.

Now you've created your own hilarious MAD LIBS® game!

FIRST PETS

COLOR _____

ADJECTIVE _____

NOUN _____

ADJECTIVE _____

NOUN _____

PLURAL NOUN _____

NOUN _____

NOUN _____

SILLY WORD _____

PERSON IN ROOM _____

ADJECTIVE _____

PERSON IN ROOM _____

PERSON IN ROOM _____

ADJECTIVE _____

NOUN _____

ADJECTIVE _____

VERB _____

ADJECTIVE _____

MAD LIBS®

FIRST PETS

When an American president gets elected, the entire family moves

into the _____ House—including their _____
             COLOR   ADJECTIVE

pets. Our first _____, George Washington, had seven
                          NOUN

_____ hounds, horses, and even a parrot that said, "Polly
ADJECTIVE

want a/an _____." John Quincy Adams owned silkworms
              NOUN

that made _____ for his wife. Zachary Taylor kept a horse
         PLURAL NOUN

on the front lawn of the White _____. Calvin Coolidge
                          NOUN

owned enough animals for a zoo, including a pygmy_____,
                                       NOUN

a pair of birds named _____ and _____, and
                    SILLY WORD   PERSON IN ROOM

even a/an _____ wallaby. John F. Kennedy had two
            ADJECTIVE

hamsters named _____ and _____. More recently,
            PERSON IN ROOM   PERSON IN ROOM

President Clinton had a/an _____ cat named Socks, who
                      ADJECTIVE

didn't get along with their Labrador _____ named
                              NOUN

Buddy. So now you know how _____ politicians learned
                      ADJECTIVE

to _____ like cats and dogs—from their _____ pets!
  VERB   ADJECTIVE

MAD LIBS® is fun to play with friends, but you can also play it by yourself! To begin with, DO NOT look at the story on the page below. Fill in the blanks on this page with the words called for. Then, using the words you have selected, fill in the blank spaces in the story.

Now you've created your own hilarious MAD LIBS® game!

THE KING OF BUTTERFLIES

PLURAL NOUN _____

ADJECTIVE _____

NOUN _____

ADJECTIVE _____

ADJECTIVE _____

NUMBER _____

ADJECTIVE _____

PLURAL NOUN _____

PLURAL NOUN _____

ADJECTIVE _____

ADJECTIVE _____

PLURAL NOUN _____

ADJECTIVE _____

PART OF THE BODY (PLURAL) _____

MAD●LIBS®

THE KING OF BUTTERFLIES

The monarch butterfly, with its distinctive black and yellow

_____, is one of the most _____ insects on
　　PLURAL NOUN　　　　　　　　　　　　　　　　ADJECTIVE

the planet. But it doesn't start life as a beautiful _____.
　　　　　　　　　　　　　　　　　　　　　　　　　　　　　　NOUN

A monarch egg first hatches into a/an _____ caterpillar
　　　　　　　　　　　　　　　　　　　　　ADJECTIVE

that spins a/an _____ covering made of silk called a
　　　　　　　　ADJECTIVE

cocoon. Over a period of _____ weeks, the caterpillar
　　　　　　　　　　　　　　NUMBER

turns into a/an _____ butterfly. When the monarch
　　　　　　　　ADJECTIVE

is able to spread its _____, it flies away to feed on a
　　　　　　　　　　PLURAL NOUN

variety of _____, including milkweed, red clover, and
　　　　　PLURAL NOUN

other _____ flowers. Monarchs are especially noted
　　　　ADJECTIVE

for their _____ migrations across the country and,
　　　　　ADJECTIVE

upon occasion, across the Atlantic and Pacific _____.
　　　　　　　　　　　　　　　　　　　　　　　　PLURAL NOUN

In flight, these _____ butterflies are a sight for sore
　　　　　　　　ADJECTIVE

_____!
PART OF THE BODY (PLURAL)

MAD LIBS® is fun to play with friends, but you can also play it by yourself! To begin with, DO NOT look at the story on the page below. Fill in the blanks on this page with the words called for. Then, using the words you have selected, fill in the blank spaces in the story.

Now you've created your own hilarious MAD LIBS® game!

SNAKE SCARE

PLURAL NOUN _____

SILLY WORD _____

PLURAL NOUN _____

ADJECTIVE _____

PART OF THE BODY _____

VERB ENDING IN "ING" _____

ADJECTIVE _____

ADJECTIVE _____

NOUN _____

PART OF THE BODY _____

VERB (PAST TENSE) _____

NOUN _____

PART OF THE BODY (PLURAL) _____

ADJECTIVE _____

NOUN _____

NOUN _____

PART OF THE BODY _____

VERB _____

MAD LIBS®

SNAKE SCARE

In my opinion, snakes are the scariest _____ on the planet.
<small>PLURAL NOUN</small>

My fear of snakes began when I was away at Camp _____
<small>SILLY WORD</small>

one summer. We were seated around a campfire roasting

_____ on sticks when I became very tired and decided
<small>PLURAL NOUN</small>

to go back to my _____ cabin to catch some shut-
<small>ADJECTIVE</small>

_____. I was snug in my _____ bag when
<small>PART OF THE BODY</small>   <small>VERB ENDING IN "ING"</small>

I suddenly felt something _____ touching my leg. At first
<small>ADJECTIVE</small>

I thought it was a/an _____ dream, but then I heard a
<small>ADJECTIVE</small>

hissing like a boiling tea _____, and felt something
<small>NOUN</small>

slithering up my _____! I _____ at the top of
<small>PART OF THE BODY</small>   <small>VERB (PAST TENSE)</small>

my lungs and was out of my _____ in a split second. I ran
<small>NOUN</small>

as fast as my _____ could carry me and dove into
<small>PART OF THE BODY (PLURAL)</small>

the _____ pond, hoping to ditch the snake. To my
<small>ADJECTIVE</small>

embarrassment, it turned out to be a harmless garter _____.
<small>NOUN</small>

But today, just the thought of a snake's scaly _____ and
<small>NOUN</small>

rattling _____ makes my skin _____!
<small>PART OF THE BODY</small>   <small>VERB</small>

MAD LIBS® is fun to play with friends, but you can also play it by yourself! To begin with, DO NOT look at the story on the page below. Fill in the blanks on this page with the words called for. Then, using the words you have selected, fill in the blank spaces in the story.

Now you've created your own hilarious MAD LIBS® game!

FELINE PHARAOHS

ADJECTIVE _____

ADJECTIVE _____

PLURAL NOUN _____

ADJECTIVE _____

NOUN _____

PLURAL NOUN _____

ADJECTIVE _____

NOUN _____

VERB ENDING IN "ING" _____

ADJECTIVE _____

PART OF THE BODY _____

PLURAL NOUN _____

ADJECTIVE _____

ADJECTIVE _____

NOUN _____

PLURAL NOUN _____

NOUN _____

MAD LIBS®

FELINE PHARAOHS

In the ancient land of _____ mummies and _____
ADJECTIVE   ADJECTIVE

pyramids, it was great to be a cat. All of today's cats are descended

from those ancient _____ of Egypt. Beginning as a wild
PLURAL NOUN

and _____ species, the cat was quickly domesticated
ADJECTIVE

and became a symbol of grace and _____. Kings, queens,
NOUN

and even common _____ discovered that cats made
PLURAL NOUN

_____ companions. Before long, felines became revered
ADJECTIVE

in Egyptian society. Every Egyptian _____ believed
NOUN

that if you saw a cat while you were _____ seeds, you
VERB ENDING IN "ING"

would have a/an _____ harvest. Images of cats were
ADJECTIVE

seen on everything from jewelry for the _____ to
PART OF THE BODY

cat-shaped _____ that women wore in their _____
PLURAL NOUN   ADJECTIVE

hair. Many homes had _____ 14-karat _____
ADJECTIVE   NOUN

cat statues. Egyptians even mummified cats, so that their owners

could spend the afterlife with their beloved _____!
PLURAL NOUN

Isn't that the _____'s meow?
NOUN

From MAD ABOUT ANIMALS MAD LIBS® • Copyright © 2009 by Price Stern Sloan,
an imprint of Penguin Random House LLC, 345 Hudson Street, New York, NY 10014.

MAD LIBS® is fun to play with friends, but you can also play it by yourself! To begin with, DO NOT look at the story on the page below. Fill in the blanks on this page with the words called for. Then, using the words you have selected, fill in the blank spaces in the story.

Now you've created your own hilarious MAD LIBS® game!

DOWN ON THE FARM

PERSON IN ROOM (FEMALE) _____

ADJECTIVE _____

VERB ENDING IN "ING" _____

NOUN _____

PLURAL NOUN _____

NOUN _____

ADJECTIVE _____

PLURAL NOUN _____

PLURAL NOUN _____

ADJECTIVE _____

ADJECTIVE _____

PLURAL NOUN _____

PERSON IN ROOM _____

ADJECTIVE _____

PART OF THE BODY _____

NOUN _____

ADJECTIVE _____

MAD LIBS®

DOWN ON THE FARM

My summer vacation on Aunt _____'s farm

_____PERSON IN ROOM (FEMALE)

has been fun, but it's also been a lot of _____ work.
_____ADJECTIVE

This morning, as usual, I woke up as the rooster was

_____, and ate a hearty _____ of
VERB ENDING IN "ING"   NOUN

_____ and syrup, with eggs freshly laid by the
PLURAL NOUN

farm _____. Then, I went out to the _____
_____NOUN   ADJECTIVE

barn to do my chores. I fed and groomed the horses, brushing

their _____ and cleaning their _____.
_____PLURAL NOUN   PLURAL NOUN

I also cleaned their _____ trough, which smelled
_____ADJECTIVE

like _____ _____. Finally, I milked
_____ADJECTIVE   PLURAL NOUN

_____, the cow. I sat on a/an _____
PERSON IN ROOM   ADJECTIVE

stool beneath the cow's _____, and filled an
_____PART OF THE BODY

entire _____ full of fresh milk. Yup, just another
_____NOUN

_____ day down on the farm!
ADJECTIVE

From MAD ABOUT ANIMALS MAD LIBS® • Copyright © 2009 by Price Stern Sloan,
an imprint of Penguin Random House LLC, 345 Hudson Street, New York, NY 10014.

MAD LIBS® is fun to play with friends, but you can also play it by yourself! To begin with, DO NOT look at the story on the page below. Fill in the blanks on this page with the words called for. Then, using the words you have selected, fill in the blank spaces in the story.

Now you've created your own hilarious MAD LIBS® game!

QUEEN BEE

PLURAL NOUN _____

ADJECTIVE _____

NOUN _____

VERB _____

ADJECTIVE _____

ADJECTIVE _____

NOUN _____

ADJECTIVE _____

ADJECTIVE _____

PLURAL NOUN _____

TYPE OF LIQUID _____

PLURAL NOUN _____

NOUN _____

PLURAL NOUN _____

ADJECTIVE _____

ADJECTIVE _____

MAD LIBS®

QUEEN BEE

The following is an interview with a Bee Bee C bee reporter and a

Queen Bee, to be read aloud by two _____.
PLURAL NOUN

Q: We are here with Her _____ Highness, the Queen
ADJECTIVE

_____, who has agreed to _____ with
NOUN   VERB

us today. Your Highness, describe your _____ hive.
ADJECTIVE

A: I am proud to reign over forty thousand _____ bees
ADJECTIVE

who work around the _____. You know what they
NOUN

say, "As _____ as a bee!"
ADJECTIVE

Q: What are some _____ bee facts that we may not know?
ADJECTIVE

A: Well, I lay over two thousand _____ a day. Other
PLURAL NOUN

bees do everything from making sweet golden _____
TYPE OF LIQUID

to pollinating _____. And each bee has its own
PLURAL NOUN

unique _____ so that I can tell them apart.
NOUN

Q: Any other _____ of wisdom for this _____
PLURAL NOUN   ADJECTIVE

reporter?

A: Honey, _____ words may sting you, but just *bee* yourself.
ADJECTIVE

From MAD ABOUT ANIMALS MAD LIBS® • Copyright © 2009 by Price Stern Sloan,
an imprint of Penguin Random House LLC, 345 Hudson Street, New York, NY 10014.